THE MINDSET
OF A TEEN

ROBENS CHERY

Principle House Publishing
www.principlelife.org

The Mind

n. the part of a person that thinks, reasons, feels decides, etc. what a person thinks or intends: opinion, desire, purpose, etc. the ability to think or reason; intelligence; the act of remembering; memory.

Library of Congress Cataloging-in-Publication Data

ISBN # 978-0-98352553-0 (Boy version)
ISBN # 978-0-98352554-7 (Girl version)

©2011 Robens Chery

Vocabulary appearing in this book are from Webster's new world dictionary and Encarta World English Dictionary.

Publisher: Principle House Publishing
            P.O. Box 190453
            Lauderhill, Florida 33319
            www.principlelife.org

Printed by: HCI Printing and Publishing
            Deerfield Beach, Florida

Cover Design by Joel Martin and Robens Chery
Interior design and formatting by Dawn Von Strolley Grove

CONTENTS

DECISIONS

n. the act or result of deciding; Firmness of mind; determination.

Decision making is one of the hardest things a teen will face. With all the pressures from society, friends, parents, and classmates, decision making and •deciphering advice are critical. When it comes to making the right decisions, some teens are failing big time. From my experience, it doesn't seem like many teens think enough about their future. Living for today is the only thing on their minds. The future is an afterthought; coming only after a terrible decision has been made and •consequences start rolling in, then common sense comes to mind.

Growing up, my parents placed a lot of •emphasis on the decisions I made, be it in my relationships, education, or life in general. They •instilled in me that whatever I chose to do, it would affect me, my future, and ultimately my whole family. I remember that statement as clear as day. My whole family will be affected by the decisions I make! That was big for me. I tried my best to make the correct decisions concerning my life so that at the end I would be happy and my family would be proud. Be very careful of the decisions you make today, because they will shape your future in one way or another.

I have seen some teens struggle in their relationships with their parents, friends, boyfriends, girlfriends, education, and finances because of the choices they have made in the past. Some of them have never recovered from their past mistakes and some of them have never forgiven themselves. Their decisions have become a •stumbling block to their future. Every decision that we make in life will affect us in a positive or negative way.

Have you ever made a bad decision and found yourself spending a •significant amount of time and energy trying to fix it?

I had a 10th grade student in my class during my second year of teaching at the high school level. She was very quiet and did all of her assignments. She was never the type that needed attention from others, so it seemed. She always had questions regarding life choices and relationships. She was always upbeat and eager to learn. After several weeks I noticed her •attitude had changed, the way she dressed, the way she talked, the way she walked—it all started to change. It really became a concern to me because the changes were not like her. I asked her why she was acting indifferent. One of her classmates screamed out, "She has a boyfriend now and she's head over heels for him. She doesn't even have time for her friends anymore." I pulled her to the side and explained to her how important it is for her to make the right decisions concerning her relationships, and not to •conform or be like everyone else. She nodded her head and went on to the next class.

A couple of months later she arrived to class crying and upset. I knew exactly what was wrong with her because I have seen this •scenario play out too many times. When I asked her what was wrong, she told me about a decision she made, and one she was •regretting greatly. She went on to explain how her boyfriend had broken her heart.

"What happened?" I asked. She explained to me how she thought the young man she was in a relationship with loved her and would do anything for her. "He told me he loved me Mr. Chery and I believed him. We were so close and I thought I loved him too. One day he came to my parents' house (Where are the parents? Are they at work? Maybe this young girl chooses to disobey her parents' rules by having boys over). We sat on the couch and he asked me to have sex with him because that's what people do when they love each other. I told him that I was a •*virgin* and I wanted to stay that way. I told him that I was not ready for sex and wanted to wait. I also told him if he really loved me like he said he did, he wouldn't force me to do something I really didn't want to do."

She went on to say "He was sad, angry; he told me I did not love him. He got up, slammed the door and went home. The next day I asked him why he left, he said he wanted to share something with me but I wouldn't. He said he loved me so much; he wanted to know if I loved him. I felt bad because I really cared for him. Deep down inside I wanted to have •sex with him but I knew I was not ready. I was confused about what to do. I did not know how to feel, I felt cornered with my feelings and emotions."

"Then I noticed quite a few girls started to flirt with him and he was •flirting back. That got me very upset and jealous. I didn't know what to do. I didn't want to lose him—we spent so much time together. I knew exactly what I had to do to keep him! So I decided to give him what he wanted—to have sex with him. So we planned to do it at my mother's house. I was so afraid and •nervous. *(Where are the parents?)*"

"He came over. He started kissing me and touching me in places I never thought would feel this way and we did it. It hurt so much, physically and emotionally, but I did it for him. He

2

held me and told me he loved me. I was hurting and crying, but happy at the same time. I got what I wanted—a boyfriend. I could not stand to lose him to anybody!"

"I was so happy! I never felt that way about anybody. I felt •loved! A couple of days passed and I started to notice a change in him, a change in his •personality. He didn't call as much, he didn't walk me to all my classes like he used to, and worst of all, I notice his friends were staring and laughing at me whenever I would walk by. I felt like he shared with his friends what we did together at my mother's house. I had to •confront him about the whole situation; I could not handle it anymore. I felt so ashamed. The way his friends looked at me they had to know something."

"I called him up and wanted some explanation for his behaviors first of all, and why his friends were laughing and carrying on towards me. I asked him if he had shared what we did with anyone. He put his head down and told me the one thing I didn't want to hear; he said he no longer wanted to be with me. He said he didn't think it was working out! After hearing those words, so much anger came over me, so much rage. I had given him something that was so •precious to me, something that I never gave to anyone else. I felt so bad, so used, so low, so dirty, so hurt. I knew better Mr. Chery; you talked about decision making all the time. How could I be so stupid? I wanted to fight him!"

(SHARING) *"I have made some terrible decisions in the past and I regret most of them."*
—11th grade student

Reflection *(in your own words)*

_____

_____

_____

_____

_____

_____

I pulled her to the side and gave her a hug explaining that one bad decision did not have to ruin her whole life. I explained to her that her experience could •potentially make her a person who will have issues with relationships or she would no longer care about herself or others. I shared, that in my opinion, she did not want to continue having sex with someone else trying to replace the guilt. I also suggested to her that she should speak to her parents or a counselor just to make sure she would be ok in the future.

I don't know to what depth this "knuckle head" destroyed her •self-worth, her •self-esteem, or to what extent the decision to do something she was not ready to do will affect her. I don't know how she will view relationships going forward, but I know she was hurt! Every time I saw her, I asked her how she was doing. After a few weeks, I noticed she was smiling again and had a different •mindset of what's important and what is not. (She had another boyfriend in two weeks).

Ladies, you have to be careful who you give yourselves to. Most teenage boys are only looking for one thing—trying to get in your pants. The question is, are you looking for the same thing? I know in the past, young men received a bad rap when it came to sex, however throughout my experiences, young ladies are also looking for that one thing and sometimes they are the ones pushing up on the young men. In some instances, "it goes both ways."

As you can see, the decisions we make in our relationships can change our lives. I have many more stories that I could tell you. However, I believe you got the point from that story. I believe if every teen would stop and think about the decisions they make and the consequences of these decisions, their futures will have a better chance of succeeding. Not just in our relationships, in everything: education, attitudes, values, finances, just to name a few.

There are consequences to everything we do whether good or bad. As teens, you have the ability to make the right decisions, in spite of what is going on in your life. "You have to come to a place in your life where you are •determined to make the right decisions in spite of how you feel or who's watching."

Many times, we spend too much time trying to correct the wrong decisions we make instead of enjoying life to the fullest. Life is full of choices. Being able to make good decisions today will determine the kind of life we live in the future, the kind of cars we drive, the kind of house we live in, the kind of relationships we have and last but not least, the kind of drama we have to deal with.

In order to make good •choices, we have to practice making them on a day-to-day basis. After all, they are your choices. Young people, make the correct choices today, not tomorrow, because today's choices are tomorrow's reality! It's never too late to start making the right decisions. Even if you have made bad choices in the past, you still have the •ability to make a difference in your life. Too many times, I notice teenagers giving up on life because of where they are and what they have done. You cannot change what you have done; you can only change what you will do. Don't give up; continue to strive and do the right things. In the long run you will be proud of where you are and where your life is headed.

(SHARING) in order for me to achieve my goals in life, I am going to have to make the right choices now so I don't regret it later. —10th grade student

Reflection *(in your own words)*

_____

_____

_____

_____

_____

_____

_____

_____

_____

_____

_____

_____

_____

_____

_____

_____

DECISION—DISCUSSION

1. If you had to say anything about the word *decision*, what would it be? _____

_____

_____

2. What is the greatest decision you have made in your life so far?_____

_____

_____

3. List some difficult decisions you have to make on a day-to-day basis?

    1. _____

    2. _____

    3. _____

    4 _____

4. Who or what has influenced your decision making? _____

_____

_____

5. Who or what do you think about when making a decision? _____

_____

_____

6. After reading this chapter, what have you learned? _____

_____

_____

7. If you had to change anything, what would it be? _____

_____

_____

_____

_____

DEFINITIONS

Decipher: _____

Consequence: _____

Emphasis: _____

Instilled: _____

Stumbling Block: _____

WRITE A SENTENCE USING EACH WORD.

Significant _____

Attitude _____

Conform_____

Scenario _____

Regretting_____

WRITE A PARAGRAPH USING THESE WORDS:

Circumstances—Confront—Flirting—Nervous—Precious—Personality

_____

_____

_____

_____

_____

_____

_____

_____

_____

_____

_____

DECISION

S	U	S	N	M	X	G	S	N	P	W	E	I	T	C
O	E	P	I	X	I	U	R	O	M	Y	C	N	N	H
D	C	C	Y	S	O	N	T	H	T	T	N	S	O	O
H	E	L	N	I	A	E	D	I	P	A	E	T	R	I
S	C	T	C	A	N	H	L	S	B	L	U	I	F	C
T	Z	E	E	T	T	A	P	I	E	H	Q	L	N	E
Z	R	Z	I	R	N	S	L	M	X	T	E	L	O	S
P	U	A	Z	O	M	I	M	V	E	A	S	E	C	S
N	L	K	S	Y	T	I	C	U	F	F	N	D	L	L
X	U	R	R	Y	Z	V	N	C	C	Z	O	P	L	T
R	E	H	P	I	C	E	D	E	M	R	C	T	G	U
P	H	Y	G	K	T	U	B	F	D	E	I	L	X	P
K	W	J	H	F	U	V	M	J	Q	O	P	C	I	W
R	E	G	R	E	T	T	I	N	G	V	C	B	J	N
T	C	H	Q	C	O	N	F	O	R	M	U	Y	D	K

ABILITY	CHOICES	CIRCUMSTANCES
CONFORM	CONFRONT	CONSEQUENCE
DECIPHER	DETERMINED	EMPHASIS
INSTILLED	MINDSET	PERSONALITY
POTENTIAL	PRECIOUS	REGRETTING

REFLECT ON THIS CHAPTER

(Write your thoughts below)

_____

_____

_____

_____

_____

_____

_____

_____

_____

_____

_____

_____

_____

_____

_____

_____

_____

_____

_____

_____

_____

_____

_____

_____

_____

_____

_____

IDENTITY

n. who or what a person or thing is; the fact of being a certain person or thing.

This is one of the biggest problems teens will face during their •transition from adolescence to adulthood. They are trying so hard to figure out who they are, whom they like, and what they like. Many of them are confused about their gender and sexuality even though their •anatomy clearly describes who and what they are.

During the teenage years your body goes through many changes; body parts grow, voices get deeper and •hormones run wild. It's a tough time for them. In my experience, I noticed many of them lose their sense of identity and direction. They question authority, parents, teachers, and even their religion becomes an issue.

One of the biggest sources of confusion during this stage is what they see on television. Their parents raise them one way but society and the entertainment industry •counteract those values. Television shows say that it is okay for a man to dress like a woman and it is acceptable for a beautiful young lady to want to be a boy. Whatever society promotes, they accept; in other words, society and television play a big part in creating an identity for our youth.

Look at MTV, BET, and all the hype channels. Teens watch these channels and mimic what they see. They imitate the wardrobe, style, lingo, and decision making of their favorite stars. They worship these individuals, not knowing that what they see most of the time is just a show or a front to persuade their fans to purchase their merchandise. Many of them don't own the cars, jewelry, houses and other accessories that are on the videos. Nevertheless, our teens are •determined to emulate whatever society is applauding. They are determined to make it according to the entertainment hype, and most of them lose their true •identity in the process.

I taught at a school where a young man occasionally dressed like a woman. He would have make up on, a dress, and high heels. I really wanted to speak to him to see where his mind was. I wanted to consider the cause of his wanting to dress like a girl. Maybe he was raised by women or maybe he was abused as a younger child. Some teens will identify themselves based on their experiences in life. Whatever, or whomever has had the most impact in their lives, they will identify themselves as that. When a teen is dealing with an identity crisis, tracing their •upbringing is the best place to see how and why they identify themselves in this way. Many times we see someone like that and immediately start calling that person names and •condemning or shaming them. This kind of behavior does not help the situation. This will only add fuel to an already confused individual's fire. We MUST STOP the hate crimes in our schools and communities.

I knew a young girl who was raped by her boyfriend when she was in the ninth grade. Because of that experience, she resents •intimate relationships. However, the occurrence created a desire and a level of promiscuity within so strong, she cannot figure out how to stop having sex. She said, "Sex means nothing to me. It's just something I do." No feeling, no emotion, just sex. I am concerned that if this continues, she will never find her true self and she will always have issues with relationships. As long as the people she's in relationships with just want sex, she will do fine. When the opportunity for a committed relationship appears, she will struggle because she only identifies with her experience. I tried my best to explain to her that she does not have to identify with her past; however I believed she needed some professional help. The school counselor and her family were informed about the situation. She ended up graduating from high school, and I believe she joined the army or the navy.

When you walk around school you may notice many young ladies dressing like boys. They cut their hair to look like a boy. They even walk like a boy. Why? They are trying to find themselves and •appearance is one way to express their identity.

Young people, do you really know who you are? Or are you too busy trying to be something or someone else? I understand you are searching for your identity, I understand you are searching for what makes you happy, but don't lose yourself in the •process. Sometimes whatever you allow yourself to become during your adolescent years, may confuse who you really are or something you have to live up to. Even when you realize that what you have worked so hard to become is really not who you are within.

I had an eleventh grader in my class that I knew from the church I attended. After a few weeks I noticed his appearance, language, and grades changed •dramatically. I asked him to come see me during my planning hour. When he came to my class, he knew exactly what I was going to say to him—you could see it on his face. I asked him why all the changes. He said, "This school was different. When he looked around the hallways he saw kids cursing, fighting, and completely disrespecting authority. Because I wanted to hang out with them and fit in, I started to identify myself with them. Please don't tell anybody that I go to church with you, this would mess up my rep." I was shocked to hear that from him; I thought this was the perfect time for some advice.

IDENTITY—DISCUSSION

1. In your own words, define the word *identity*? _____

_____

_____

2. How do you identify yourself?_____

_____

_____

3. Who do you look up to and why? _____

_____

_____

4. How do your friends identify you? _____

_____

_____

5. What do you do to express your identity? _____

_____

_____

6. After reading this chapter, what have you learned? _____

_____

_____

7. Is there anything you want to change about your identity? Explain._____

_____

_____

_____

_____

_____

_____

DEFINITIONS

Transition: _____

Counteract: _____

Determine: _____

Condemning: _____

Upbringing: _____

WRITE A SENTENCE USING EACH WORD.

Intimate _____

Appearance _____

Dramatically _____

Recommend _____

WRITE A PARAGRAPH USING THESE WORDS:

Accepted—Intend—Dramatically—Relationship—Identity

_____

_____

_____

_____

_____

_____

_____

_____

_____

_____

_____

_____

IDENTITY

ACROSS

2. A way that grabs the attention and causes an excited, shocked, or startled reaction
5. To suggest something as worthy, of being accepted, used, or done
6. To plan for the future
8. The human body
9. A series of actions directed toward a particular aim
12. The care and training a person receives while growing up

DOWN

1. Who or what a person or thing is; the fact of being a certain person or thing
3. The way somebody looks or seems to other people
4. Having, involving a close personal relationship
7. Showing firmness or a fixed purpose
10. To prevent something from having an effect
11. A process or period in which one undergoes a change

REFLECT ON THIS CHAPTER

(Write your thoughts below)

_____

_____

_____

_____

_____

_____

_____

_____

_____

_____

_____

_____

_____

_____

_____

_____

_____

_____

_____

_____

_____

_____

_____

_____

_____

_____

_____

_____

MUSIC

n. the art of putting tones together in various •melodies, •rhythms, and •harmonies to form compositions for singing or playing on instruments. Music can be a source of great joy and great pleasure.

From uploading to downloading, after the early 2000's, music moved beyond being simply played on CDs, and light years away from the old record albums. Every teenager, and many of their parents, has some kind of device that plays music. Everybody's got an iPod or phone that stores his or her own favorite music. Music has become one of the major •essentials a teenager has to have. Music is a major component that teens use today to deal with their issues or to show their peers they are hip or have "swag".

(SHARING) "I couldn't have a good day without my music. Whenever I'm in a stressful mood, the music calms me down and makes my day better." —11th grade student

Reflection *(in your own words)*

_____

_____

_____

_____

_____

_____

_____

_____

_____

The iPod has become part of their wardrobe. Without music, many teens would actually have a bad day because most of them can •relate their issues with what they are listening to. As a teacher, everyday has become a challenge. I'm •constantly asking students to put their music away, stop singing that song, stop acting like that rapper or that singer.

Music is so deeply rooted in the 21st century generation's lifestyle that some students ask to listen to music during a test so they can relax. I taught a young man once who wanted to use his iPod during the FCAT (Florida Comprehensive Assessment Test). He was so nervous about the test he needed something to calm him down or to give him the •confidence he needed to accomplish the task (of course he was not allowed).

When some teenagers go through struggles in their lives, whether in school or at home, they find an artist or a rapper that sings something along the lines of their issues and plays that artist's music all day long. They can really •relate to what the artist is saying. I remember my freshmen year in college; I was going through some tough times with a young lady I was dating. I had to find a song that was •relevant to what I was going through, and when I found that song I never stopped playing it. I can still hear the melody to this day. However, I think some of them have taken their love for music a bit too far. For example, I see teens trying to •emulate an artist in their dress, their talk, and even in the artist's beliefs. When it comes to character and morals, they will duplicate their favorite artist.

Some kids will come to class and do all their work, as long they have their music. As a teacher, you can get a lot out of your students with music. In my classes, students are able to listen to music if they earn it. They have to behave and complete all assignments. Clear rules and expectations must be established, because you have some that want everyone else to hear or listen to what they are listening to.

One of the things I cannot understand is how they memorize all of the songs on the radio or on their iPods' but they can't remember the vocabulary words for the spelling test. The same •methods used to learn the songs can be used to learn in school. I always wondered if rappers or singers sang or rapped about education, how successful our teens would be, since music has so much of an influence on them. I know some school systems have already •incorporated music into their curriculum. However, I believe our students would be more excited to hear a rapper like Little Wayne from Cash Money Records, rapping about social studies and science, or Snoop Dog rapping about reading and math, or Nikki Minaj singing about literature. That would be the day; just a thought! I've noticed some companies already going towards that concept, however, I think it can be more of a success if major artists are involved.

What music is on your iPod? What music is on your phone? The type of music you listen to is the type of character you display. If you listen to "F---" this and "F---" that, eventually you will start speaking that way and acting that way. We have to be very careful about what we are listening to these days; music can be very •influential to our •attitudes, our feelings, our emotions, and even our actions. Many teens know exactly what music to play when they are with their boyfriends or girlfriends and what music to play when they are hanging out with their peers. You can tell by their reaction, which music is their favorite. If their song comes on the radio, they stop everything, start singing, dancing and say saying "That's my song!"

(SHARING) *"Music is my life. I don't know what I would do without music. I am going through so much right now; music is the only thing that keeps me together and to have hope even though I don't see where hope will come from."* —12th grade student

Reflection *(in your own words)*

_____

_____

_____

_____

_____

_____

_____

_____

_____

_____

_____

MUSIC—DISCUSSION

1. What's your definition of *music*? _____

_____

_____

2. In what ways has music affected your life? _____

_____

_____

3. What would you do without music? _____

_____

_____

4. Have you ever used music to deal with what you are going through? If yes, explain. _____

_____

_____

5. Who is your favorite artist, and why? _____

_____

_____

6. After reading this chapter, what have you learned? _____

_____

_____

7. What would you change? _____

_____

_____

_____

_____

_____

DEFINITIONS

Incorporated: _____

Attitude: _____

Inappropriate: _____

Music: _____

WRITE A SENTENCE USING EACH WORD.

Melodies _____

Rhythms _____

Harmonies _____

Essentials _____

Constantly _____

WRITE A PARAGRAPH USING THESE WORDS:

Confidence—Relate—Relevant—Emulate—Methods

_____

_____

_____

_____

_____

_____

_____

_____

_____

_____

MUSIC

```
C   E   E   Q   S   H   E   N   W   P   Z   E   C   D
O   T   T   S   I   E   O   M   C   B   D   S   E   S
N   A   N   M   S   M   I   Z   U   U   Z   T   G   X
S   I   A   E   R   E   P   D   T   L   A   V   Y   U
T   R   V   T   U   H   N   I   O   R   A   J   P   C
A   P   E   H   A   C   T   T   O   L   W   T   O   R
N   O   L   O   Y   T   T   P   I   C   E   N   E   T
T   R   E   D   A   Z   R   K   Z   A   F   M   Y   S
L   P   R   S   L   O   Q   R   A   I   L   J   M   P
Y   P   V   P   C   R   E   R   D   O   R   S   O   L
L   A   I   N   F   L   U   E   N   T   I   A   L   D
F   N   I   W   A   T   N   R   H   Y   T   H   M   S
L   I   J   T   E   C   N   E   M   B   R   T   T   A
F   T   E   S   E   I   N   O   M   R   A   H   L   E
```

ATTITUDE	CONFIDENCE	CONSTANTLY
EMULATE	ESSENTIALS	HARMONIES
INAPPROPRIATE	INCORPORATE	INFLUENTIAL
MELODIES	METHODS	RELATE
RELEVANT	RHYTHM	

REFLECT ON THIS CHAPTER

(Write your thoughts below)

RELATIONSHIPS

n. the condition of being related; connection; dealing with two people.

I have experienced teaching on every level of education from Elementary to High school. I have seen a lot of things, some not so •favorable. Nevertheless, I find myself year after year going back to •impart, care for, teach, do whatever it takes to •inspire the students I come in contact with. Some things are just too much for one person to handle.

How can a third grader understand what sex is? Why is a fifth grader having sex in the bathroom? When I look down the hallways, why do I see middle and high school students pregnant? What is going on? Where are they getting their information? Who is laying their •foundation? What are they going through? So many questions to be answered! Sex, sex, sex, sex. It's everywhere!

By the time teens reach high school, they have lost the norms and values that the older generation has •instilled in their hearts. This is influenced by what they see on television, in their peers, or in their environment. I believe some parents take a lot of time and effort instructing their teens on what is right, what is wrong and how to conduct themselves. Unfortunately, society and the latest trends are winning.

I found out that most of our teens are confused when it comes to relationships. Why are they thinking about that anyway? Is it their upbringing? They hear the •conversations of their older siblings regarding relationships. Is it that there are no parents at home to impart into our teens? Or are teens trying to replace the lack of love and understanding that burns from within? Whatever the reason, teens are confused when it comes to relationships.

Some of our young men are trying to prove to their friends they are tough or that they are truly a man. One way they are proving this is by having as many girlfriends as possible. I have witnessed some boys disrespecting girls—they sleep with them, lie to them, cheat on them, and so on.

Having a lot of girlfriends doesn't prove you are a man. Treating women with no respect proves nothing. As a matter of fact, it is the opposite. I always instruct my male students to treat women the same way they would want someone to treat their mothers or sisters—with respect and •dignity! I am an adult now and I have never cursed at my mother or said anything rude or •disrespectful to her. Never! I was walking down the hallway one afternoon and noticed a group of young boys cursing and yelling at a young girl. I knew one of the boys, so I pulled him to the side and asked him, "Why were you talking down to this young girl?" he said, "Because she deserved it." I asked him if his mother did something wrong to his dad, if it is ok for his dad to curse and yell at his mom. He said, "no, and that he would be very upset at his dad for speaking to his mom in that manner." I replied to him that the same goes for this young girl.

•Degrading women is not the way to go.

As young men, you are the future of this twisted society. Without you, the cycle of father-less homes and "baby momma drama" will continue to affect our families and our •communities in every aspect of life. As young men, you should be leaders, not followers of what everyone else is doing. You can change your community, your school, and everything around you. Find a positive role model, and model yourself after them. You can be that person of •integrity!

I also found out these young men are searching for an identity, their fathers, and guidance. When these desires are not met, they get discouraged and assume no one cares. They go with the trend of how women are treated in society. They use excuses to justify their actions. I came across a tenth grade student one year. He had a mean •demeanor, always had a rough answer to everything. One day I asked him why was he so angry? His answer was, "Why you care?" He went on to say that I walk around the school acting like I care, but I don't. I asked him, "Is this why you walk around here skipping class and don't care about anybody because you feel no one cares about you?" He placed his head down but gave no answer. Every day I tried my best to say something to him, something positive. I wanted to build some kind of •communication with him since he was not in my class. One day he came to my class and asked if he could have a word with me. I told him to come back during my planning hour and told him to get back to class. The bell rang for the next class and he was already standing at my door.

He started by saying "One day you ask me why I don't care about anything. I want to talk to you about that! When I was in the eighth grade, my •father left my mom to raise me all by herself. I don't know why he left, but he did. I thought he was coming back, but he never did. I am so angry at him because of what he did. I think he left because he doesn't love me or my mother. I cried a lot in the beginning; I was sad and could not figure out why he left. I don't cry anymore! When I ask my mom about it, immediately she starts to cry. She told me that my father had other plans that did not •involve us. I used to be a very good student with good grades. Now I am just here!"

"I figure since I don't have anything to be happy about why should I care or smile." I told him that I was glad he shared his story with me. I also told him that he had a great future in front of him. Don't allow what happened to you in the past to stop you from becoming who you want to be in life. You are smart and •intelligent. Use your pain as a motivation to accomplish your goals. I asked him what was his goal before this happened.

"I wanted to be a basketball player," he said. Since I played basketball, we started to develop a friendship around school. We talked about everything. He brought his mother to school one day during an after school program. It was great to meet his mother. We talked for a while. I wanted her to understand what her son was going through and how to encourage him to continue to •strive for the future. We must instruct and encourage our teens to •overcome hardship.

In my experience, when the time comes to be in a relationship, some will only do what they see, think, or assume to be correct according to society, upbringing, or experiences. Some of them have seen their mothers being beaten, cursed at, or mistreated. They grow up thinking that's the way to do things. They assumed its okay to have three or four girlfriends and the girls should only have one partner. She would be •considered a whore if she had more. Having three or four boyfriends is not a popular thing for young ladies but it is for young men. This world is truly bugged. Young men, we have to do better.

(SHARING) *"Most teens, mainly girls, start having sex because they feel alone and want someone to love them."*
　　　　　　　　　　　　　　　　　　　　　　　　　　　　　　　—12th grade student

Reflection *(in your own words)*

_____

_____

_____

_____

_____

_____

Sex is at the •forefront of our society. Sex is in everything, from television to cartoons, movies to music. And let's not forget the internet. Most of our teens are into sex not because they really want to be, but rather what they •assume they can gain from it. The American Public Health Association (APHA) reports that one of the biggest reasons that teenagers engage in sexual activity is because they think their peers are also having sex. Most of them are looking for attention, •companionship, and someone to love them.

Some teens will become attached to people who show them affection. Most of the time, that person is not the one for them. Anybody can show affection, but not everybody that shows affection really cares. What is going on in our homes today? Are parents caring for their teens the way they should? Are they too busy working and taking care of their needs "instead of their seeds"? If parents don't take care of their children, then someone else will. Buying those clothes for school or putting food on the table is not enough to show that you care. Parents must take the time to show true •affection. Tell them how much you love them and are proud of them. Encourage them; they are looking for your affirmation. If the only time they hear your voice is when they are doing something wrong or when they fail, they will conclude that you only acknowledge their failures and not their successes. There are men today still searching to prove to their fathers that they are not failures, instead of spending their time trying to fulfill their purpose in life.

Some teens are also confused about how to express their feelings and emotions. As children, they were taught that men don't cry or men don't express their feelings and if they do, they are looked at as being soft or weak. That's the last thing they want to be •perceived as. Some teens will do whatever it takes to protect their feelings from being hurt. They will fight, argue, lie, cheat, and stay away from •committed relationships to protect their feelings and emotions. Yes, teenage boys have feelings too; they may not express them, but they are there.

(SHARING) *"I will never give my whole heart to a girl. Every time I do, something bad always happens."*

—11th grade student

Reflection *(in your own words)*

_____

_____

_____

_____

_____

_____

I have also seen respectable young men with focused •mindsets on education, who have respect for their peers. These young men had strong upbringings. They choose to do the right thing in spite of what they went through or are going through. They understood that they didn't have to prove themselves to their peers. They are confident in who they are, how they are perceived and they are proud of it. These young men are strong in their decision making, they are willing to change the status quo and the bad reputation young men have received over the years.

So young men, you don't have anything to prove about your manhood. Just be yourself and understand that you have the power and the •ability to create your future. Do it the right way and you will not regret it later. The people you are trying to impress are not really your friends because if they were, you would not have to prove who you are.

When I was in high school, I played basketball and was part of many organizations. I didn't find myself in a lot of trouble because I knew who I was and I didn't allow anyone to •redirect my •perceptions. I knew what I wanted out of life and I was not going to allow any-one to take that away from me. It was hard at times, but I kept my mind and actions together. Society says, having a lot of girls is cool and acceptable. Jumping from one relationship to another is the way to go. For some odd reason, it's cool to skip school or just not follow the rules. Even though I failed a few times, I knew inside of me I had to get back to doing the things that would help me reach my goals.

The schools I had a chance to be a part of, I see the relationship struggles in some of the young girls. They are really in trouble. They are dying for a father figure. First of all, they are striving to be loved by their parents and also their peers. They want to be accepted, loved, and noticed. Can we still have meaningful relationships in spite of what happened in the past or what society is showing? I believe so! By the time our young ladies reach high school, most of them have lost their most important •asset (their •virginity). Most of them are happy about losing such a great attribute. There's so much pressure on our teens today to lose their virginity before graduating from high school.

Mostly everyone is doing it and if you are not doing it, you are not "cool or hip". When I was in school, if you were a virgin, you would be called "stuck up". They don't know how beautiful they are and how much they are •worth. They don't know they are the mothers of the next generation. Maybe if they understand who they are and how much they are worth, things would be different. Maybe they would act differently, talk differently, and dress differently. But their conduct is •promiscuous, loose, "bout it," and they are not worried about themselves or their futures. This •senseless conduct must stop! You cannot continue to live this way and expect to have a great future. I understand you've been through a lot or you want to be accepted. However, you are worth more than just a five minute thrill, or someone else's amusement. Young ladies, think about yourselves for a moment; think about your future.

By keeping yourself away from sexual activities, you will protect yourself from diseases, emotional and physical hurt. Last, but not least, you will protect your name. According to the Center for Disease Control (CDC), there are 19 million new STD infections recorded every year. Fifty percent of these cases happen to young people between the age of 15 and 24. The American Social Health Association (ASHA) reports that half of all new HIV infections occur in teenagers, and about 2/3 of seniors in high school have had sex.

I believe giving •advice to most teens and expecting them to follow it is easier said than done. Why would you say that Mr Chery? Girls who have been raped, abused, depressed, or hurt in their past relationships, whether victimized by family or others, become •vulnerable. They will build a wall between them and the world. They will only allow a certain few to get close, and the ones that they do allow to get close have to face other walls that protect their deepest feelings and desires. They assume that •lust is love. Love to them is based on how they feel, who can satisfy their needs or who can show sympathy towards what they have experienced.

I want to be the first to say that feelings and emotions are never the same. True love is not based on feelings or emotions. It is based on commitment, loyalty, unselfishness, account-ability, unity, and so much more. True love is wanting to be with someone just the way they are; wanting to •commit to someone with no strings attached. True love is not based on what the person can give you or you can get out of the relationship. Some teens are confused about their emotions. The effect of their confusion may lead to teen •pregnancy, diseases and more pain and hurt than they started with. Let me ask you a question: If you knew that you have a chance to get pregnant or contract •HIV, would you allow your feelings or emotions to get in the way? Maybe you are not thinking about that at that moment. Think about this. The Center for Disease Control says that one third of girls get pregnant before the age of 20.

I was working at a middle school where students were having sex in the bathrooms through-out the day. In the bathrooms? Yes, in the bathroom! How can a young girl or a young boy be brave enough to have sex in the bathroom and not be worried about who would see them or talk about them? What are they going through? Nowadays, these types of bathroom activi-ties are even happening in elementary schools. What is going on in the mind of that young man? Is it, "I'm just getting some "booty" in the bathroom to tell my friends about" or is it deeper than that? Is that act fulfilling more than just the physical? The extreme that teens will go to get what they want sometimes, can be dangerous. After all, the whole school would know about it and because of what is going on in the inside, that's the least of their worries. The need for acceptance, •acknowledgment, approval, and bragging rights is more impor-tant. As long as their needs are met, then they will deal with the •consequences later. On the website SolitaryRoad.com owned by James Miller, Miller states that "Children (both young children and teenagers) do many things out of the desire to be accepted by their peers." One of the consequences is that kids in school will talk about what you do, good or bad. No one is safe from word of mouth. Everything and anything that happens in school or outside of school has a chance of being exposed. Do you want to be exposed and end up having to deny the facts about your behavior or are you going to be careful with your decisions? This way there's nothing to expose! Think about that for a moment. You don't have to prove anything to anybody. You can be accepted just the way you are. The next time you think about doing something just to be accepted, don't. You are worth more than that.

I have also noticed young ladies with their head on their shoulders. They dress appropriately and their actions say a lot about their •character and what they want to be in life. These young ladies clearly understand that the decisions they make now can impact their future positively or negatively. They are •strong-minded; they don't allow people or friends to dictate their actions. I can truly say that they have a greater chance of succeeding because of how they carry themselves. I believe these young ladies made up their mind to take control of their lives. Maybe they have a great support group around them or maybe they have been through and decided enough is enough. I was reading some facts on teen pregnancy. One fact states that teenage mothers are more likely to drop out of school. Those that remain single parents also score lower in both math and reading. These are some alarming stats.

Most of the time, the obsession for attention usually leads to more problems and more hurt. I believe the relationships that some teens are partaking in will in eventually lead to bad marriages and will continue the high rate of marriages ending in divorce. What do you mean? For teens, the average relationship lasts about a week or two. Throughout the school year, the average teen has had at least six to twelve relationships. Most of which are intimate. At this rate, by the time our teens graduate from high school, they would have been in so many relationships they would assume this is how relationships should be. Jumping from one relationship to another, sleeping with one person this week and another the next. This may be one of the reasons why our divorce rate is so high! Kids have been practicing these •principles since middle school.

(SHARING) *"Trying to finish school and deciding which boy is right for me. I'm also •concerned about the many diseases that are in the community and getting pregnant too early. Moreover, I'm trying to stay focused and be a successful person."* —11th grade student

Reflection *(in your own words)*

_____

_____

_____

_____

_____

_____

_____

_____

_____

_____

_____

_____

_____

Young people, don't allow what happened to you in the past redirect how you behave in the future. Many times, we allow what happened to us in our past relationships, hurts, and disappointments to •contribute to how we treat others in the future. The people that we come in contact with in the future should not have to pay for what someone did to us in our past. It's not fair. Before you take on new relationships and commitments, close the doors on your past relationships, good or bad. They need to be released and let go, that way you can have meaningful, •constructive relationships. How can you do that you may ask? Well, first of all, you have to forgive the person that hurt you. I know it's hard, but it must be done. Believe me, you will feel so much better. •Forgiveness allows you to move forward without the anger and wanting to not care about yourself and others. Second, you must forgive yourself. Many times we don't release ourselves from the mistakes we have made. Forgiving ourselves gives us a sense of •freedom and a sense of self-worth. Third, we must try our best to not hurt someone else in the same way we were hurt. When I got married three years ago, I promised my wife that I would do my best to never treat her the way I was treated in my past relationships. The only way I was able to do that is through forgiveness.

Moreover, the experiences you •encountered in the past should not contribute to who you are now. One other way for us to have meaningful relationships in the future is to practice having meaningful relationships now. Many times we assumed we can live our lives one way for many years and change it whenever we want to. All I am saying is to live your life now how you want to live it in the future.

Growing up, I knew what I wanted in a relationship. Whenever I had a chance to be in a relationship, I tried my best to practice what I wanted in the future. My relationship with my wife has a greater chance of succeeding because of what I have practiced as a teenager.

Many people have allowed their experiences to be their •identity, which in the long run will continue to cause more •confusion physically, mentally, and emotionally.

(SHARING) *"I don't know how to deal with my past. So much hurt, so much pain. Nobody understands the misery I had to go through when I was being abused by my uncle for several years. I will never forget that!"* —12th grade student

Reflection *(in your own words)*

_____

_____

_____

_____

_____

_____

RELATIONSHIPS—DISCUSSION

1. What does the word *relationship* mean to you? _____

_____

_____

_____

2. Have you had any bad experiences with any of your relationships? _____

_____

_____

3. How's your relationship with your parents? _____

_____

_____

4. How do your past experiences affect your views on relationships? _____

_____

_____

_____

5. How do you feel about the word promiscuous? _____

_____

_____

_____

6. Do you know the consequences of having sex at an early age? _____

_____

_____

_____

7. What have you learned from this chapter? _____

_____

_____

DEFINITIONS

Favorable: _____

Impart: _____

Inspire: _____

Foundation: _____

Instilled: _____

WRITE A SENTENCE USING EACH WORD

Conversation _____

Dignity _____

Disrespectful _____

Degrading _____

Integrity_____

Contribute_____

Character_____

Consequence_____

Spontaneous _____

WRITE A PARAGRAPH USING THESE WORDS:

Communication—Father—Involve—Considered—Affection—Committed

_____

_____

_____

_____

_____

_____

RELATIONSHIPS

```
Y  C  V  Y  O  U  A  R  E  I  V  E  A  L  U  S  E
T  H  U  A  B  L  E  V  N  A  L  L  U  E  S  U  L
I  A  L  Y  O  U  R  S  S  P  E  L  P  E  F  O  B
R  R  N  G  W  J  P  L  I  H  U  I  N  V  D  U  A
G  A  E  W  H  I  O  C  L  H  H  E  E  I  K  C  R
E  C  R  N  R  O  N  G  Y  S  V  N  S  C  F  S  O
T  T  A  E  J  I  Q  Y  N  I  J  R  F  K  W  I  V
N  E  B  B  R  S  H  O  G  I  E  I  P  Y  T  M  A
I  R  L  P  C  Q  I  R  A  S  D  R  P  T  N  O  F
A  B  E  E  F  N  O  W  P  A  E  A  Z  I  W  R  D
U  D  G  P  A  F  A  E  F  G  D  X  R  N  H  P  Y
L  M  I  P  S  P  C  B  N  Q  S  E  A  G  C  V  V
M  A  M  O  I  T  Z  A  W  O  R  T  H  I  E  N  F
D  O  J  X  F  I  N  X  V  P  M  J  E  D  W  D  B
C  M  K  U  E  C  N  E  U  Q  E  S  N  O  C  M  Q
Z  Q  L  V  Y  H  T  E  B  N  X  S  T  W  W  A  K
K  V  S  Y  C  F  L  I  L  T  B  T  O  P  I  U  F
```

CHARACTER	COMPANIONSHIP	DEGRADING	DIGNITY	FAVORABLE
INTEGRITY	CONSEQUENCE	DISRESPECTFUL	INSPIRE	FORGIVENESS
PREGNANCY	PROMISCUOUS	VULNERABLE	WORTH	PRINCIPLE

REFLECT ON THIS CHAPTER

(Write your thoughts below)

_____

_____

_____

_____

_____

_____

_____

_____

_____

_____

_____

_____

_____

_____

_____

_____

_____

_____

_____

_____

_____

_____

_____

_____

ATTENTION

n. the act of keeping one's mind on something; the act of noticing; observation.
Thoughtful care; kindness and affection

Attention, attention. Everybody wants attention from their •peers. Many times, trying to get the attention of others leads to much more than just being seen or heard. I asked one of my middle school classes this question: Why do teens strive for attention from their peers? The answers were amazing. One student •confirmed that the reason teens strive for attention is to get noticed, to be in the *in crowd,* for the opposite sex, •competition, and because they are looking for acceptance—acceptance from their peers and acceptance from their parents. Their parents? Yes, their parents.

(SHARING) *"I don't get any attention at home. My parents are never there, and whenever they get home, they are always fighting and screaming at each other."* —10th grade student

Reflection *(in your own words)*

_____

_____

_____

_____

_____

_____

_____

_____

First of all, let's break this topic down into two sections: boys and girls. Let's start with the girls. Girls are wearing fewer clothes these days to bring attention to themselves. They will do almost anything to capture the boys' attention. Girls are wearing clothes so tight that the shape of their bodies show from every angle. (Think about that statement for a moment).

The jeans are so low that their gluteal cleft are showing and they are loving it. All of this for some attention? Is it worth it? I remember taking a young girl to the front office because her private part was showing through her pants. Word has it, that's how she dresses. I asked her if she was aware of her •attire? She would not answer. I think she liked the attention she was getting from the boys.

There's truly a reason behind her actions. Most girls believe in order to get the attention of a particular boy, they have to show some skin and flirt a little. Only if they knew what a little skin would lead to! One thing I have found is that they are not thinking of the actions; their whole focus is on getting him to look, talk, and like what he sees. There are more middle and high school kids walking around in the hallways, at the malls, even at church, with their breasts out showing their •cleavage. All of this to get the attention of others. *If a boy has to see your body parts to talk to you, then he is not the one.* The young man's agenda is to get to know your body, not you. The sad thing about the last statement is that most of the girls don't really care if the boys want to get to know their body parts, as long as the attention is on their bodies instead of other girls.

(SHARING) *"I like the attention I get from my friends. I think it's because of the way I dress. I love to dress and the way it makes me feel. It's sexy."* —11th grade student

Reflection *(in your own words)*

_____

_____

_____

_____

_____

_____

_____

The attention they get is enough to make them feel important, •accepted, and popular. The sad thing is, it doesn't stop there. Girls will go as far as having sex to get their attention or to keep a particular person. Some girls only date athletes because of the attention they would get from just being with him. The girls that go after the athletes usually get hurt. Male athletes, at that age are not trying to be in a relationship. They know being on lock down will only take away their chances of getting all of the ladies.

Ladies, be for real. Yes, you are getting his attention but are you looking at the •cost? The pain? The agony? The pressure? Take a moment and think about what you are doing, who you are doing it with. He doesn't even like you! These kind of relationships will never last because it was based on your body and •vulnerability. At the end of the day, he still doesn't know you. He never intended to get to know you; your body was his only •concern.

That's sad. Ok, ok, ok, let's talk about the boys for a while; we will come back to the girls.

Boys are also searching for attention. They will do what they assume is cool or what their peers will cheer about. When you look in the school system from elementary to high school, the problems are the same. Young men are walking around with their pants half way down their butts and being cool about it because it is accepted in our society, especially in the hip-hop community. There's nothing cool about showing your butt to other men. Anyways, that's another chapter. Continuing with our topic, boys will spend most, if not all their money, on how they look because they know that if they dress a certain way or talk a certain way, or behave a certain way, they will eventually attract the attention of the opposite sex.

Throughout my experiences in the school system, getting the attention of their peers has become their number one goal. I thought we sent our children to school to get an education, not to worry about how they look and what they wear. Most of the boys I've come across dress very well but they can't •comprehend a reading passage. They are failing most of their classes. How they look takes •priority in their day-to-day lives. Learning becomes secondary or for some, learning is last on the list. They will cheat their way through school but they will look good doing it.

Young men are having sex just to say they did it. It is no longer cool to be a virgin for a boy or girl. If you are a virgin in today's society, people will look at you as if something is wrong with you. As for the girls, it is not popular to have your name associated with having sex; the opposite goes for the boys. The more sex a boy has, the more attention he gets from his peers. And because they know they will get •noticed if they are having sex, they •strive to fulfill that goal by having as many partners as possible. Ladies watch out!

(SHARING) *"Girls love tough boys. I like the attention I get from them. They make me feel important."* —11th grade student

Reflection *(in your own words)*

_____

_____

_____

_____

_____

_____

_____

In my second year of teaching, I •encountered many characters in the classroom and in the hallways. Many of the boys were trying to look tough so no one would mess with them. Some of them were doing it to get the girls, since girls like "bad boys". Some of them are really tough because they are from the streets. When you pull them to the side in a one on one conversation, you notice these kids are just trying to fit in. I remember an incident where the toughest kid in the school was in the process of fighting another kid in my hallway. I pulled the kid in my classroom and started •communicating with him. I wanted to know why he wanted to fight everybody and why he didn't care about his life or anyone else. His answers were shocking.

First, he started crying. Crying? Yes, crying. He told me that his father was in jail and his mother was always beating and yelling at him, whenever he did anything wrong. He went on to say that his mother is never at home because she has to work two jobs, and he has to take care of his younger sister, who does not listen. He feels that if anyone •messes with him, he has to do or say something so no one would think that he's soft. I clearly understand where he was coming from. However, I asked him what he wanted to be in life. He said, "I want to be a designer!" I explained to him that the way he was acting will make it hard for him to achieve his goals in life. I told him that in order to achieve anything in life, he had to have a good education and a great attitude.

You cannot allow •circumstances to dictate how you talk, act, and treat others. I understand that you are frustrated with the situation at home, but acting the way you are acting in school will only make matters worse. I explained to him that he is the example for his younger sister. Whatever you do she will do, so be careful how you act because someone else may be watching. He told me that no one ever broke it down to him like I did and he promised to correct his behaviors, in-spite of what was going on at home. It's amazing what a good conversation can do for a child.

He is now telling others to get to class and creating a •positive environment in the classrooms and in the hallways. This is how we make a change in the hearts and minds of our teens. Give them a way out of their struggles because they are struggling. What you see on the outside is never what is going on in the inside.

Back to the girls. Many are loud, rude, and have foul mouths. They will say anything just to look like they are the "badass chicks" in school. It's more than just attention for the girls; they have a lot on the line. School is the place where they can showcase who they are and how sexy they can be. They want to be accepted, they want to feel •secure, and they want to be noticed. Where are the fathers?

I was at a high school where dressing became a •fashion statement. Girls walking down the hallways with heels, make-up, designer purses. Their jeans were so tight and low! The hallways became a club scene or a photo shoot for somebody's rap video. All of that just to get the •attention.

I knew a young girl in the eleventh grade. She would have on the hottest gear with matching shoes, purse, hair, and jewelry. I asked her one day, "How long does it take you to get ready in the morning? She told me she has everything prepared the night before, that way all she has to do is get ready. When I asked her about her grades, she put her head down and started walking down the hallway. To her, school was a fashion show, not a place for learning. What's the point of looking good if you can't spell or pass the FCAT? What's the point of looking good and the only vocabulary you know are curse words.

ATTENTION—DISCUSSION

1. What do you do to get *attention* from your peers? _____

_____

_____

2. How do you feel when you get the attention you are looking for? _____

_____

_____

3. What do you do or how do you feel when you don't get the attention you are looking for? ____

_____

_____

4. How far would you go to get someone's attention? _____

_____

_____

5. Do you get enough attention from your parents? Explain. _____

_____

_____

6. After reading this chapter, what have you learned? _____

_____

_____

7. List some of the things the kids in your school are doing to get attention.

　　1. _____

　　2. _____

　　3. _____

　　4. _____

　　5. _____

DEFINITIONS

Peers: _____

Competition: _____

Fashion: _____

Cleavage: _____

Vulnerability: _____

WRITE A SENTENCE USING EACH WORD

Concern _____

Comprehend _____

Priority _____

Strive _____

Encounter _____

WRITE A PARAGRAPH USING THESE WORDS

Communicating—Circumstance—Secure—Eventually—Fashion

_____

_____

_____

_____

_____

_____

_____

_____

_____

ATTENTION

```
Y  E  V  E  N  T  U  A  L  L  Y  N  E  E  Q
C  T  Y  U  H  F  F  C  P  F  O  N  C  N  J
N  O  I  F  A  E  N  R  B  I  B  R  N  C  Q
T  O  M  L  O  W  I  I  T  P  T  E  A  O  N
Y  J  I  P  I  O  T  I  R  G  L  C  T  U  Y
G  G  F  H  R  B  T  J  G  W  R  N  S  N  H
V  N  C  I  S  E  A  P  F  N  E  O  M  T  A
Y  A  T  T  P  A  H  R  E  J  A  C  U  E  V
M  Y  X  M  H  E  F  E  E  K  T  C  R  C
V  O  O  D  R  X  E  W  N  N  R  O  R  X  N
Q  C  X  U  C  P  Z  T  F  D  L  S  I  H  Z
M  X  C  S  T  R  I  V  E  B  P  U  C  I  V
D  E  G  A  V  A  E  L  C  B  C  F  V  F  J
S  V  L  K  H  W  D  G  E  B  F  G  Q  I  L
G  N  I  T  A  C  I  N  U  M  M  O  C  L  S
```

CIRCUMSTANCE   CLEAVAGE   COMMUNICATING

COMPETITION   COMPREHEND   CONCERN

ENCOUNTER   EVENTUALLY   FASHION

PEERS   PRIORITY   SECURE

STRIVE   VULNERABILITY

REFLECT ON THIS CHAPTER

(Write your thoughts below)

_____

_____

_____

_____

_____

_____

_____

_____

_____

_____

_____

_____

_____

_____

_____

_____

_____

_____

_____

_____

_____

_____

_____

_____

_____

_____

EDUCATION

n. the act or work of educating or training people;
the things a person learns by being taught.

Education is the most important thing a teen can have or •achieve in today's society. Without education, they will •struggle, the economy will struggle, and at the end, the country will struggle. Children are our future, if they are not being •equipped for the future, where will we be ten years from now as a people, as a country? Education has to be the number one focus in the minds of our teens. So why are they dropping out of school? Do they still believe they can achieve?

(SHARING) "My education is very important to my family and me. If I want to be anything in life, my education will open that door." —12th grade student

Reflection *(in your own words)*

_____

_____

_____

_____

_____

_____

_____

I remember when I came to this country, my parents sat my brothers and I down and explained to us the reason we were here in America. I am •originally from Haiti. In the late 80s, there weren't any functioning schools in Haiti because of the •political struggle the country was facing at the time. We wanted to attend school, but unfortunately we couldn't. I remember when my brothers and I went to school, only a handful of students were there. No teacher, no students, just emptiness. It felt weird! It felt unreal. We would watch the news and would see people being burned with tires covering their bodies from head to toe. People were afraid to leave their homes and afraid to send their kids to school. Three months passed and there were no changes, still no school, still hearing gunshots, and the news was the same. The memories still live inside of me as vivid as it was when I lived there. Sometimes I wonder what happened to my friends that didn't have the same •opportunity I had.

My parents understood the magnitude of a great education. They decided to move the family to Florida for a better life and a better chance for an education. It was not easy to let go of everything that they worked so hard for and built for so many years to move to America. However, the future of their children was at stake. My father worked for one of the biggest •manufacturers in Port-Au-Prince, Haiti, while my mother ran a boutique store near the house and taught sewing. All of their labor was done to help the family succeed. They gave up everything so we could have better opportunities in life, and •education would give us access to those opportunities.

My mother went ahead of us to find a home for us to live in. I remember sitting at the Port-Au-Prince airport crying because my mother was leaving. After three months, we joined her in South Florida. I remember arriving at the airport; it was amazing! The lights, the people, everything was different.

After a few weeks, my father had to return to Haiti to sell everything that we owned and return to Miami for good. It was tough not having him there. This was the first time I had to experience the feeling of not having my father around. I started playing some of his music I found in a box just to have the feeling that he was with me.

He came back after a few months, and that's when things became •difficult. My father had to work in a freezer of a super market and my mother as a cashier. Can you imagine that? He went from manager to stocking meat in the freezer; she went from teacher and storeowner to cashier. How many parents would give up everything for their children? I will always remember what my parents did for us; they gave us a chance to succeed.

I share that story with you to express the importance of education, and how my parents sacrificed so their children could be successful in life. Every time I felt like quitting or giving up, I thought of the •sacrifice my parents made for me. I also thought about my friends in Haiti that never had the opportunity I had.

The issues I faced in Haiti were completely different from the issues teens face here in America. I thought these kids were •spoiled and didn't have a clue of the opportunities available in America. When they wake up in the morning, they are picked up by a school bus with leather seats and air conditioning, while they freely enjoy expensive iPods and other electronic gadgets. When they arrived at school, they are served hot breakfast in a fully air conditioned building. Nice classrooms with seats and again—air conditioning. Then it's free midday lunch . . . you get the picture. What else does a child need to succeed? As I got older, I understood even though they had everything they would need to succeed in school, they were still dealing with a lot as teenagers.

(SHARING) "I don't even think about school most of the time. So much is going on in my life. Sometime I just want to give up." —11th grade student

Reflection *(in your own words)*

_____

_____

_____

_____

_____

_____

_____

_____

They are going through so much in their personal lives that they would •forfeit education or drop out of school without thinking that this is the most important time in their lives. My question always is, what can I do to •encourage my students to realize that education is the most important thing they can achieve today? When teens care less about their education and more about the kind of clothes and shoes they wear, or who's cute and who's not, you question yourself: What I mean by that is, are parents monitoring the amount of television their kids are watching? Are parents spending time doing homework with their children? Or are they assuming that the homework is being done? If the guardian doesn't stress the importance of education, then the child will place the same effort as the guardian. Is education the number one thing at home?

As a teacher, you notice everything in your classroom. I noticed a young lady who sat in my classroom daily and never turned in any assignments. She was in class but her mind was somewhere else. No •productivity! I asked her to stay after class one day to address the issue. I asked her, "Why aren't you turning in any assignments?" Her answer was, "I have time, it's just the first quarter. Give me a break Mr. Chery!" I was very •disturbed by her answer. Who in their right mind would do nothing the first quarter and start doing their assignments in the second or the third quarter? What she doesn't understand is that the assignments that were due in the first quarter can no longer be made up because she was not sick, or missed school for a long period of time. Those were the choices she made. What is going on in her mind? Maybe her mind is on other things that she •assumed to be more valuable than her education.

This kind of behavior goes on every year and most of them have failed trying to catch up. Young people, the first semester is the most important semester in the school year. You have to make the most of it by establishing a strong base with your grades and your teachers in the first semester. If anything happens, your teachers will give you the benefit of the doubt that you are a student who takes education seriously. Most students think backwards. A smart student would do all of his/her work in the beginning of the school year and relax at the end of the school year. Nevertheless, if you were to ask teachers all over the country to compare the amount of assignments kids turn in at the end of the year than in the beginning of the school year, the numbers would be astounding. There are other factors that tie in to low performance. Sometimes, it is due to their lack of performance in the beginning of the school year, or even as far back as the middle schools years. Teens become •disruptive, angry, depressed, and eventually give up on life. According to C. Jerald, in his book "Dropping Out is Hard to Do", he states that, "most dropouts are already on the path to failure in the middle grades and engage in behaviors that strongly •correlate to dropping out in high school. Various researchers have identified specific risk factors, such as low attendance or a failing grade, which can identify future dropouts—in some cases as early as sixth grade."

All of the issues are not just related to •laziness. Most kids drop out of school because they are not doing as well in their grade level or because they are having some issues at home. According to the Alliance For Excellent Education, 2009, "There is no single reason that students drop out. Research indicates that difficult transitions to high school, deficient basic skills, and a lack of engagement serve as •prominent barriers to graduation." Some teens assume they can make it in life without education or a high school diploma. You cannot even get a job at a local restaurant without a high school diploma [What are they thinking]? I have seen good kids go bad and drop out of school because what they deal with in and out of school is too much to bear. This, in the end, confuses their judgment on what is truly important: Their education!

Another •component to a teen's lack of focus on their education is some of them have to work to help with bills and other things. Some teens get out of work at twelve in the evening and have to get up at five in the morning to be ready for school. When asked why don't they just quit the job and focus on school, their answers are that they have to work to take care of their siblings and themselves. That's sad!!! Many of the students want to do well in school; unfortunately their situations don't permit them. School has to be the top •priority. If it's not, our teens will suffer for it later. It's tough for a student to have to work and go to school at the same time. But when the pressure is on from the family, the decision to work and attend school becomes easier to make.

When I was in high school, I wanted to work. Not that my parents wanted me to, but I wanted some extra money in my pocket. I wanted to feel like a man. I wanted to wear the Jordan shoes instead of LA gear. I wanted to go to the movies without asking my parents for money. However, my parents •insisted that I focus on my education. They did their best to address my •constant needs as they appeared. They also explained to me the dangers of working and going to school at the same time. Even though I wanted to make money, even though I wanted to look "fly" and feel like a man, I understood that my education was more important. My education will carry me into the future. My education will give me a chance to have all of the •materialistic things I desired as a teen. The choice was to look good now or live better later. Without an education, I could only work or make a certain amount of money and I did not want to make that kind of money for the rest of my life. So I decided not to work and focus on my education. That was the best decision I have ever made. Because of education, I received a scholarship to play basketball all five years in college. I saved my parents thousands of dollars just because I decided to make education my priority. Some teens don't have the luxury of having both parents in their lives to support them during their adolescent years. They may feel the need to work to •appear to be as good or popular as others. My advice to you is, in spite of everything that's not going right in your life, try your best to make education your priority. If you have to work, work just enough hours to help out and •devote yourself to your studies. Have an open communication with your guardians about the importance of your education.

(SHARING) *"I am trying to do well in school and want to come to school every day. I am tired in the morning and most of the time I just don't want to come. But, I have to remember that I want to be something in life."* —11th grade student

Reflection *(in your own words)*

_____

_____

_____

_____

_____

_____

_____

Sometimes it's not about choices; it's deeper than the eyes can see. Some teens lost their •confidence a long time ago because of what they've been through and what they are going through now. Many of them don't believe they can achieve their goals in life. When they look around, they may be the only one in their family that ever •attempted to graduate from high school. When they look around, they notice the guy down the street who never went to school but makes more money than a teacher would, in a lifetime. When they look around them, they see what the older women are doing to make money and how they are treated. If they are already struggling in school, then they will take the •alternative and turn to the streets to make it. For some, that may be the only thing they know.

I live in a state where teens have to pass the FCAT (Florida Comprehensive Assessment Test), a state required assessment test, to graduate from high school. Since the FCAT was •implemented, many students have failed. Many of our struggling students experience pressure, the weeks leading up to the FCAT. Many times, all we want our students to do is learn. However, we don't spend enough time to get to know them and the real reason behind their lack of productivity.

Some of them have allowed other components to take •precedence in their lives. To some it's sex, drugs, alcohol, or gangs. For others, it's their pains from within. Some of them are from another country and they are trying to fit in. It was hard for me to fit in when I came to this country. I only knew two English words and I used these two words everywhere I went. These two words were "shut up". I told everybody to "shut up," sometimes with a smile and sometimes with a frown until one day I almost got beat up for it. Then someone was kind enough to explain to me the meaning of those words.

Again I say, there is more than the eyes can see. Some teens didn't have dinner last night. Some of them may have been abused by a sibling or are having some issues at home. Other students are being •bullied either physically or verbally. Some of them just want to be accepted. Whatever the reason may be, it is hindering the progress of our youth. If I had any of the issues I just listed, it would be very difficult for me to attend school. I remember a time when I was afraid to attend school because I was being bullied because of where I came from. It was hard! I am not saying it's an excuse; what I am saying is if we can first target the needs of a student in and out of school and find ways to help him/her deal with them, then maybe, just maybe they would be better students. They would be more effective, •motivated, eager to learn, and better positioned to achieve their dreams in the long run.

EDUCATION—DISCUSSION

1. What do you think about when you hear the word *education*? _____

_____

_____

2. What do you want to accomplish with your education? _____

_____

_____

3. What are the struggles you have encountered in the process of getting your education? _____

_____

_____

4. Are you going to allow these struggles to stop you from achieving your goals? Explain. _____

_____

_____

5. Do you want to go to college? If yes, where? If no, explain. _____

_____

_____

6. Are you willing to do everything to graduate? Explain. _____

_____

_____

7. What comes to mind when you hear about kids from other countries that don't have the same

opportunities you have? _____

_____

_____

8. After reading this chapter, what have you learned? _____

_____

_____

DEFINITIONS

Achieve: _____

Struggle: _____

Equipped: _____

Opportunity: _____

Manufacture: _____

WRITE A SENTENCE USING EACH WORD

Education _____

Difficult _____

Sacrifice _____

Spoiled _____

Forfeit _____

WRITE TWO PARAGRAPH USING THESE WORDS

Encourage—Productivity—Disturbed—Disruptive—Laziness—Prominent—Priority—Constant—Confidence—Attempted—Alternative—Implement—Precedence

_____

_____

_____

_____

_____

_____

_____

_____

EDUCATION

Unscramble each of the clue words.

Copy the letters in the numbered cells to other cells with the same number.

TOIPORTPNYU

17	14				20	5		19		21

FIRSICCAE

26			16			9	22	

OTRIFFE

	15		35	28		

GURNOAEEC

10			24			1		

UDPITTICOVRY

			7	8							36

VUIRIEPSTD

	6							

LAIZESNS

					2	32	11

IPITORRY

	18				27	3

SACBOELT

	12	33	13			11

NIFENCDEOC

	4		31	23		30		34

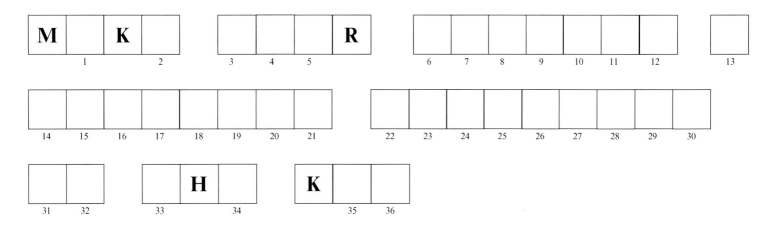

Unscramble each of the clue words.

Copy the letters in the numbered cells to other cells with the same number.

REFLECT ON THIS CHAPTER

(Write your thoughts below)

_____

_____

_____

_____

_____

_____

_____

_____

_____

_____

_____

_____

_____

_____

ACCEPTANCE

n. the act of accepting; the condition of being accepted; approval or belief

Being accepted in school, at home, or in the neighborhood is a major component in the lives of a teen. In the five year period I worked within the public school system I've had many conversations with students. I believe most of them feel like they are not accepted at home. The only place they can be accepted is at school. At school they don't have to be themselves, they can be somebody else. They can •pretend to be the person they really want to be. They often go to the extreme to be accepted by their peers even if their actions are not •appropriate.

(SHARING) *"Sometimes, I don't think about what I do to be accepted. I just do what I need to do. I like the attention I get from my friends."*   —*11th grade student.*

Reflection *(in your own words)*

_____

_____

_____

_____

_____

_____

_____

_____

I believe acceptance is very important in the growing process of a teen. Many of them base their whole lives on the word "acceptance". If they feel they are accepted, they will no longer focus on being accepted. Most of their focus will then change to other things such as education and their future.

After two years in South Florida, I noticed the way everyone dressed, talked and reacted to situations. I wanted to be accepted by my peers, so I set out to look like them, talk like them and even walk like them. I wanted to wear the baggy pants, the Nike shoes etc . . . unfortunately, my mother was not with it. She's from Haiti and people from the island of Haiti don't play when it comes to their children's identity. They want their children to be proud of who they are and their culture. I came home one day with my pants hanging off my waist with my pimp walk saying "wassup dog" but with an accent (stop laughing). I thought she was going to kill me the way she looked at me. She pulled me to the side and told me "There's going to be no thugs in this house (She had a heavier accent than I had). You better get it together or I will get it together for you! I did not bring you to this country to start acting like somebody else." I was not from this country, but I wanted to be accepted by the people in this country. I also wanted to live to see my next birthday so I changed my •wardrobe fast. "That woman is crazy!" I yelled. I didn't act or look like my peers and because of that I didn't have many friends. I wasn't accepted because I was from another country. I wanted to be accepted, but I was •rejected most of the time.

Have you ever done anything just to be accepted? Well, my older brother did! My father had a big issue with the way we wanted to cut our hair. We were allowed to get a haircut, however, we were not allowed to get a tape or a fade. Fade was in style back then. My father said that he did not want us to change our •culture by following what people from this country are doing, referring to how they cut their hair. I know some of you are laughing right about now but it's true. We had to get a normal hair cut with no tape in the front. Many of you know if you don't tape the front of your hair after a haircut, you have what we call a "batman tape". My friends called me names every time I had a haircut. One day, I don't know what my older brother was thinking; he came home with a fade (a type of hair cut) with the side of his head bald and a fresh tape. I've got to say it was nice. I wanted one so bad but I kept •envisioning my father's belt on my back. He was walking around the house acting cool, though he was the coolest guy on the block. I believe we call that "swag" now. My mother came home first and she almost lost it. I saw her eyes turn red and she was looking for something to knock my older brother into a deep sleep. She was so upset that she told my older brother to "get rid of that hair cut before your father comes home or you will have to find another place to stay!"

My brother ran out the house to his friend's house to fix his hair. When he came back I asked him why he did it knowing mom and dad would get upset. He said he wanted to be accepted in school and that he was tired of being laughed at. I understood where he was coming from, however, I also understood my parents' belt! Many of our teens today are doing a lot just to be accepted. They are trying so hard to be cool, loved, and •acknowledged. When the time comes for them to make the right decisions in life, they struggle because their decisions will be based on whether or not they'll be accepted.

(SHARING) *"I will do anything to be accepted by my friends. They are the only real friends I got."*
                                                                —10th grade student

Reflection *(in your own words)*

_____

_____

_____

_____

_____

_____

_____

_____

Many teens join gangs because they feel more loved and accepted from the gang members than from their own •families. Whenever you ask any gang member the reason they joined a gang, their first reason is to be accepted. Often they say, "they accept me just the way I am." There is an interesting article written by Barbara Aufiero, freelance writer from New York. Barbara has a Master of Arts in psychology and worked in the health industry for almost ten years. She states that teenagers often struggle to •define themselves and their place in the world. They may choose to associate with a certain group because its members share similar beliefs, attitudes or interests. However, teens also look to others to fulfill their basic needs for such things as companionship, understanding, and emotional support. When these needs are not met •sufficiently or at all by the teen's family, they become •susceptible to joining gangs.

It took me a long time to understand that everyone is not going to accept me. I also understood that I was not going to accept everyone. Having that mindset really helped me transition from my country to America.

I had a close friend who was determined to be accepted. He was so •determined to be accepted that he would practically do anything. He started stealing, fighting, and selling drugs. He really lost his identity trying to be accepted. I had a chance to speak with him one day and I asked him what he was doing with his life? He asked why I asked him that question. I said, "Because of the way you are acting. The way you are acting will only take you to a place that will ruin your life in the long run."

Years passed. Every time I saw him he was still hanging around the same crowd doing the same thing, trying to •impress his peers.

I truly understand that we want to be accepted as teenagers, but at what cost? Are you willing to give up your identity, self-worth, and your future just to be accepted by some people that deep down inside really are not looking out for your best interest?

To make a long story short, after high school, one of his friends from the group he hung out with set him up with an undercover detective. His friend was arrested for a crime and giving somebody else up would lessen his time. His friend set him up to distribute drugs to the undercover officer and he got arrested. Everything was on camera—he had no chance of getting out of this one. He was •sentenced to 15 years in the state prison. When I talked to him, the one thing he always said was "he •regrets everything that he ever did with his so called friends."

ACCEPTANCE—DISCUSSION

1. What are you doing to be *accepted*? _____

_____

_____

2. How far will you go to be accepted by your peers? _____

_____

_____

3. If the people you want to be around want you to change who you are, would you? Explain. ___

_____

_____

4. What are your friends doing to be accepted? _____

_____

_____

5. What have you learned from this chapter? _____

_____

_____

6. In your own words, define the word acceptance. _____

_____

_____

_____

_____

_____

_____

_____

DEFINITIONS

Pretend: _____ _____

Appropriate: _____

Wardrobe:_____

Rejected: _____

Envision: _____

WRITE A SENTENCE USING EACH WORD

Sufficiently _____

Susceptible _____

Determined _____

Impress _____

Regret _____

WRITE A PARAGRAPH USING THESE WORDS

Sentence—Family—Acceptance—Acknowledge—Culture

_____

_____

_____

_____

_____

_____

_____

_____

_____

_____

ACCEPTANCE

```
Y   Y   D   C   A   R   T   S   L   E   J   E   N   F   B
K   L   Z   E   E   C   E   O   R   I   L   G   O   A   K
P   W   T   G   T   N   C   U   O   B   M   D   I   M   O
Y   R   R   N   T   C   T   E   I   Y   V   E   S   I   D
J   E   E   E   E   L   E   T   P   C   C   L   I   L   E
T   V   N   T   U   I   P   J   E   T   O   W   V   Y   T
I   C   K   C   E   E   C   Q   E   Q   A   O   N   W   E
E   X   M   O   C   N   A   I   X   R   J   N   E   Q   R
A   Q   D   S   O   R   D   M   F   H   F   K   C   N   M
R   Q   U   L   D   J   J   E   Q   F   X   C   Z   E   I
Y   S   E   B   O   R   D   R   A   W   U   A   Q   G   N
A   P   P   R   O   P   R   I   A   T   E   S   C   J   E
N   W   I   M   P   R   E   S   S   X   E   M   R   F   D
F   S   I   Q   Z   N   T   B   E   Y   U   H   P   O   L
C   I   G   X   H   B   Y   F   K   V   S   A   C   U   B
```

ACCEPTANCE	ACKNOWLEDGE	APPROPRIATE
CULTURE	DETERMINED	ENVISION
FAMILY	IMPRESS	PRETEND
REGRET	REJECTED	SENTENCE
SUFFICIENTLY	SUSCEPTIBLE	WARDROBE

64

REFLECT ON THIS CHAPTER

(Write your thoughts below)

_____

_____

_____

_____

_____

_____

_____

_____

_____

_____

_____

_____

_____

_____

_____

_____

_____

_____

_____

_____

_____

_____

_____

_____

REPUTATION

***n. what people generally think about the character of a person or thing;
Good name; fame or distinction; Respected***

(SHARING) *"Reputation is the overall •quality or •character as seen or judged by people in general. It is important that a person has a good reputation whether in school, at a job or in a community because it follows you everywhere you go. Having a positive reputation will gain a person the respect that is due to them, but having a bad reputation comes with many •downfalls and failures in life. People with good reputations have the qualities of being positive leaders; they are very respectful and respected by others. They are hardworking and determined to achieve any goal possible."* —11th grade student

Reflection *(in your own words)*

_____

_____

_____

_____

_____

_____

_____

Most teens don't really think or care about their reputations during the adolescent years, but some do. Most teens just live for the moment and don't think about how they would be affected by their ways of life. On the other hand, some teens will do almost anything to build a good reputation. At the end of the day, they want to be remembered as a person with good character and •integrity. What do you want to be remembered as? The girl that had sex in the bathroom? The girl that everybody talked about in the classroom? The boy that had three or four girlfriends? The boy that dressed real good but couldn't spell?

Whatever you are doing during your teenage years will be remembered for a long time. Some of your actions will not just be remembered, but will also follow you into adulthood.

(SHARING) *"My reputation is good and I am proud that it is that way. My teachers are very respectful to me and I am respectful to them. If you ask about me in school, people will tell you that I am quiet, hardworking and intelligent. I always wear a •pleasant smile on my face and very down to earth, even though I don't care what people think of me. It is good that somebody can •recognize you or characterize you as a good student with a positive reputation."* —11th grade student

Reflection *(in your own words)*

_____

_____

_____

_____

_____

_____

_____

Let me ask you a question: What is your reputation now? If I ask your friends or just the people who hang around you about your reputation, what would they say? Are you living a life where what people say about you matters? Well, you should be. When I look around the school system, the neighborhoods, and the malls, your actions tell me that you don't care about the reputation you are putting out. Maybe you don't care about what people may say about you. People are going to talk regardless, just make sure what they are saying is not true. I have come to the •realization that most of the things that your friends are saying about you are true. Some of your classmates may be jealous of the way you dress or the way you look, but I don't think they would envy your actions or the way you •conduct yourself in school and at home.

(SHARING) "I don't actually know what my reputation is, but I think people will know and remember me as a person who kept her grades up, who didn't disrespect people unless I got disrespected, and the person who didn't mess with people. At this point, I really don't think people should look at reputation because as the saying goes, "never judge the book by its cover," meaning you can't tell who someone really is by looking at them. So I don't believe you should pay attention to reputation." —12th grade student

Reflection *(in your own words)*

_____

_____

_____

_____

_____

_____

_____

When I was in middle school, I wanted to talk to this fine, tall, sexy, dark skin, eight-grade basketball player. I did all I could to be •noticed by her. She was in my fifth period class. Every day I would plan my day around my fifth period. She was so fine! After a few days, I got the courage to go and speak to her. I found out that she also had feelings for me . . . (oh yeah)! After a few weeks of •conversation, I wanted her to be my girlfriend. I took a piece of paper and asked her if she would like to be my girlfriend and created two boxes in which she can select yes or no. Then I thought that would be too soft and cowardly, so I decided to use Valentine's Day to ask her.

Valentine's Day was just around the corner and I thought it would be a good idea to ask her during this time to be my valentine. I had it all planned out. I didn't have enough money to get new shoes, so I had to clean my LA gears (You young guys don't know about LA gears). I stopped at the flower shop and bought some flowers and a card. I was ready and scared at the same time.

When I arrived at school, one of my good friends noticed my •attire and my flowers (we called them carnations back then) so he asked who they were for. I told him they were for Christina, the girl in our fifth period. I will never forget the look I got from him when he heard who I was so ready to make my girlfriend. He went on to say that I couldn't be with her because she had a boyfriend now. Also the talk around school is that she sleeps around with everybody. All of the life that was in my flower stems wilted. It was shocking to hear what I heard about the girl that I liked. She was so fine! I could not believe this, not her!

I was supposed to meet with her after third period. I decided to cancel our meeting, but I knew I would see her during fifth period. I wanted to skip fifth period but I knew I would get in trouble with my teacher. So I decided to attend class. That day, was the longest day ever. When fifth period came about, I was confused, depressed, hurt and everything else. I walked in class and there she was sitting with her head down. She asked me what happened with a guilty look. She said, "Did Marvin say something to you?" I said yes and didn't say anything else. She wanted to explain herself but that particular day, I didn't want to hear it. I was hurt. I spent so much time and money on this girl, and all this time she was playing me.

She built a reputation so bad around school and that reputation •eventually caught up with her. Her reputation, character, and integrity were so bad; I wanted nothing to do with her. How can this be? The girl that I liked had a bad reputation! One thing I noticed; whatever happened in school or outside of school, everyone ultimately heard about it. What was she thinking? What is she going through that she cannot be with one person? Those were the questions I was asking myself. Every time I tried to talk to her about why she could not be with just one person, she would cry. She said she had watched how her brothers never got hurt in relationships because they always had more than one girlfriend. If one of them decided to leave, they would be ok. She was afraid of getting hurt, so she always had someone around just in case. I asked her had anybody left her in the past. We went through middle and high school together and she never answered that question. For some reason or another, many teens don't think sleeping around, fighting, cursing, stealing, or disrespecting adults, are •indicative of a bad reputation. Parents can help with their teen's reputation by being a good role model. As parents, teachers, and mentors we can show our teens the importance of having good character with the way they behave. Remember, our teens are watching our every move.

What good can come from these characteristics? Most teens are trying so hard to impress their peers that they would go out of their way, go out of their comfort zone, just to please their peers.

(SHARING) *"A high school reputation follows you forever, especially for girls. They have a harder time because every little thing counts. If you go out with a boy and you break up with him, he may get mad. That anger would build and lead up to a rumor being spread about you. A high school reputation is very important because it follows you. Some girls don't care about their reputation because they are trying to live the fast life. My reputation started good then I met this boy and it went downhill. If I could I would go back in time and change that because it still follows me today."* —11th grade student

Reflection *(in your own words)*

_____

_____

_____

_____

_____

We did eventually end up becoming friends again later in that school year. As you can see, nothing is a secret no matter how •secretive it was done. A time will come when your secret will •surface, then what? Are you going to deny it or are you going to conduct yourself a certain way in order for your reputation to be in good standing? Whatever you decide to do, it's up to you, no one else.

I took a survey on the word reputation in one of my classes when I taught in high school and the result was outstanding. It seemed like everyone knew exactly what the word reputation meant, but not too many were careful enough to protect theirs.

Boys, on the other hand, will do almost anything to build a reputation that will give them the •edge when it comes to the streets, school, or their surroundings. They will try to have as many girlfriends as possible, call girls •derogatory names, try to win as many fights as possible, or try to look as tough as possible, just to have a macho reputation. I believe most of these actions will lead to nothing but trouble in the long run. Once you have built a reputation, you have to keep it; you have to live up to it. If you are known to be a fighter, then that's what you do even when you don't want to. If you are known to be a player, then that's what you have to live up to.

Sometimes I've seen young men who tried to change the reputations they have worked so hard to build, but because of their peers, they continue these actions until something terrible happens. Things like suspension, being expelled from school, arrested, jail, (pregnancy), dead, and what? What is your reputation? It's never too late to change your reputation, character, or your integrity. Think about your future and think also about what you want to do in life. If what you are doing will and in some way effect what you want to become in life, then I suggest you change. You don't have to go to jail or get kicked out of school to learn that your actions matter. Stop trying to please everybody. If you don't want to do something because you know it's wrong then don't do it. Don't even think about.

(SHARING) *"Reputation is something that follows you for the rest of your life. Some people don't think about it, so they do whatever and don't believe it will come right back at them. Most high school students think that doing drugs, having sex, and failing school is a good thing. But they're wrong because all that they do now will go with them in the future."*

—10th grade student

Reflection *(in your own words)*

_____

_____

_____

_____

_____

_____

_____

Young ladies, you have to be aware of the kind of reputation you are •displaying in school and in the neighborhood. Whatever you do in school, either good or bad, will be remembered. Years later when you run into a classmate or someone who was in your school, they will remember you as the person you were at the time they knew you. Be very careful about the things you do today because what you do today will be remembered tomorrow. remember you as the person you were at the time they knew you. Be very careful about the things you do today because what you do today will be remembered tomorrow.

(SHARING) "Reputation to me is how someone's history and future is put together based on their •accomplishments or mistakes throughout their lives. Your reputation is also based on the path you take and the choices you make in your future and the choices you make in your past. You will either have a good reputation or a bad reputation. It is better to have a good reputation than a bad reputation. Having a good reputation is better because it shows that you are a good person inside and out. You have respect for yourself, you respect others, and you know what's good and what's not. Having a good reputation can bring you a bright future and a career. You will be respected by others and you will have absolutely nothing to be ashamed of. Having a bad reputation, on the other hand, is something very different. You have no respect for yourself and if you have no respect for yourself then others will have no respect for you. You will go through life making bad choices and you will always be remembered for it. What's done is done, you cannot change the past, but you can change the future. Your reputation is basically your entire life so it's important to live it to the fullest and live it right"
—12th grade student

Reflection *(in your own words)*

_____

_____

_____

_____

_____

_____

_____

_____

REPUTATION—DISCUSSION

1. What comes to mind when you hear the word *reputation*? _____

_____

_____

2. What is your reputation at school? In the community? _____

_____

_____

3. Do you care about what people think or say about you? Explain. _____

_____

_____

4. After you graduate from school, how do you want to be remembered?_____

_____

_____

5. What do your friends say about you? _____

_____

_____

6. Is there anything you want to change about your reputation? _____

_____

_____

7. What have you learned from this chapter? _____

_____

_____

_____

_____

_____

DEFINITIONS

Quality: _____

Character: _____

Downfall: _____

Integrity: _____

Pleasant: _____

WRITE A SENTENCE USING EACH WORD

Recognize _____

Realization _____

Conduct _____

Attire _____

Notice _____

WRITE A PARAGRAPH USING THESE WORDS

Eventually—Indicative—Secretive—Surface—Derogatory—Accomplishment

_____

_____

_____

_____

_____

_____

_____

_____

_____

_____

REPUTATION

QYALUTI

RASUCFE

CECHARRAT

TINGTYREI

NODCUTC

NAOSOIVCRENT

TATEIR

TALESPAN

CIEVERSET

GYATOERODR

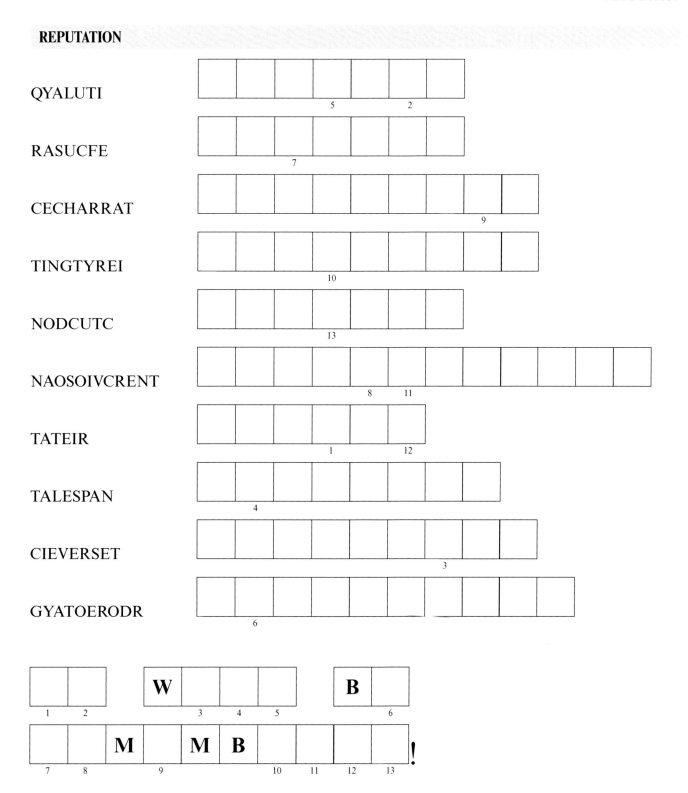

Unscramble each of the clue words.

Copy the letters in the numbered cells to other cells with the same number.

75

REFLECT ON THIS CHAPTER

(Write your thoughts below)

_____

_____

_____

_____

_____

_____

_____

_____

_____

_____

_____

_____

_____

_____

_____

_____

_____

_____

_____

_____

_____

_____

NORMS/VALUES

n. a way of behaving that is usual for a certain group.

n. the quality of a thing that makes it wanted or desirable; to think highly of.

This chapter is a big one for me. I believe one of the main causes behind our teens behavior is the lack of norms and values. I asked a group of 10th graders the definition of the word •norms and only one or two knew the meaning of the word. Everybody is doing everything, saying anything, and showing everything. Why is that? No norms or values.

Most teenagers lie on a regular basis. Lying is part of who they are. They lie so much that they begin to believe their own lies. Most teenagers don't speak when they walk into a room. Wherever you go, teens will walk by you and not acknowledge you. Well, I found out either those morals were never passed down from their parents or they are just rude because of whatever they have experienced. They don't see the value or importance of acknowledging others.

Most of our teens don't understand there is such a thing as •moral character. They don't understand that there's a way a person behaves in spite of his/her situation, pressure, or loss. I remember a quote from one of the referees' at a summer league basketball game. He said, "If you don't stand for something, you will fall for everything." There must be a •standard that we live by. Without a standard, we are on track to do anything. This is exactly what is going on in the mind of our teens. They don't have a standard that they live by. They accept whatever the world does or whatever society says is acceptable. Whatever their friends, boyfriends, or girlfriends say is ok, becomes ok.

(SHARING) "It's hard to have norms or values when everything around you is not going the way you plan for them to go. Your father got some girl pregnant and your mother is trying so hard to keep the family in place. When you see that as a young girl, you question yourself and the things you believe in."　　　　　　　　　　　—12th grade student

Reflection *(in your own words)*

_____

_____

When I was a teacher at the high school level, I came across a few young ladies and young men who had a standard on how to live, act, and get involved in relationships. They really wanted to make it in life and they understood at an early age that the way they acted would have an •impact on their success. They were respectful, kind, intelligent, and very focused.

I also came across some teens that lived by the rule, whatever happens, happens. They were open to any and everything. They didn't have a cutoff point. Sex was just something that people do when they are in a relationship. Cursing was the way that people expressed themselves either in a positive or negative way. Being rude to teachers and parents was a way of life. How can this be? How far do they expect to get in life with those characteristics? To value certain things is to understand the importance of it. To be respectful is to understand the importance of being respected. To value •abstinence is to understand the importance of your life physically, •mentally, and spiritually. You must stand for something and not allow anyone to change your views.

(SHARING) *"I value myself, and everything I do. I cannot see myself behaving the way everyone else behaves. I don't know how these girls around here do what they do! It's sad."*

—11th grade student

Reflection *(in your own words)*

_____

_____

_____

_____

_____

I was playing basketball at the gym one day and I heard a few of the young guys using a lot of foul language. Every time they would make a shot or a block, they would say the F word. I remember when I used to curse when I played basketball. I only did it to look tough or just because everyone else was doing it. It got so bad that I had to say something to them. I asked them why they •cursed so much and one of them said it's because it's part of the game. "Says who?" I replied. "Kobe Bryant!" He answered. I asked him where he got that from. He said that it was in his book. "It's in Kobe Bryant's book?" I asked.

I continued, in amazement. "He said that? Kobe Bryant, the best basketball player in the world, said cursing is part of basketball? Because I play basketball, I must curse to express myself?" I was shocked that teens are being affected by the characteristics of their •idols. I have not read the book, but I believed him. There are so many books out there twisting and confusing the minds of this generation. These books have no norms and values in the information they are conveying, and our teens are following.

There was a young lady in my class; she was a senior in high school. She had no idea of her worth as a young lady. She had no standards, morals, or character. How can this be? She gave herself sexually to everyone she dated. At that rate, by the time she graduates from college, she would have a football team •attributed to her sexual roster. She dressed a certain way assuming that was the only way she could get a boyfriend. I mean she was lost. I knew her best friend and I really wanted to talk to her. I wanted to express some degree of •values to her, and let her know how much she was worth. Clearly norms and values were the last thing on her mind. I regret not talking to her. I wonder where she is now and how she's doing in life.

Every chance I had, I tried to speak on norms and values. These two basic •concepts have so much impact on a person's character and decision making. A person who understands the values they possess, will do almost anything to uphold and live up to those standards.

So, why are most of our teens not living up to their proper moral standards? Maybe it's because they don't see them at home. We cannot expect our teens to be something they have never seen. I will never forget what a woman said on the radio one afternoon! I believe it was on Hot 105 during the Michael Baisden show, a popular nationally-syndicated talk and music program. This woman called in to the show and said, "We are trying to come up with •strategies to deal with teenagers, we should be trying to come up with strategics to deal with their parents because the fruit don't fall too far from the tree." What she was saying was stop looking at the fruit and start looking at the trees that produce the fruit. I hope everyone got that! Let us not only look at our teens, let us also look at the parents that are •responsible for our teens.

Having good character as a teen will keep you away from a lot of unwanted attention. It will keep you away from unwanted decisions and it will definitely keep you away from the things that everyone else is doing in schools, behind the cafeteria, and behind the gym. Having norms and values will allow people to trust your judgments because they can see your character and your actions. Are you practicing good character? Having a good character now will help you develop into an •upright adult in the future. It's good to start now, that way you already possess good character as you grow from adolescent to adulthood. Have you ever noticed an adult with bad character? Well it started when they were teenagers. It is so hard to stop an adult from doing something they spent their entire life doing. However, it is much easier to change a teenager. Are you willing to change? What are you waiting for? Don't allow something terrible to happen in your life before you change your norms or values. I know one thing; you can do whatever you put your mind to do, so put your mind to something positive and •productive. You don't have to do what everyone else is doing, especially when you consider that they don't know what they are doing either!

(SHARING) "My parents talk to me all the time about my character. They always say that a good character will take you far in life. I believe them because I can see it in the way they act."   —10th grade student

Reflection *(in your own words)*

_____

_____

_____

_____

_____

_____

_____

_____

_____

_____

_____

_____

NORM/VALUES—DISCUSSION

1. What do you think about the words norm/values? _____

_____

_____

2. Do you value your characters? Explain. _____

_____

_____

3. What do you value in life? _____

_____

_____

4. What are some of the things you would never do? _____

_____

_____

5. Do you value what people think about you? Please explain. _____

_____

_____

6. What can you benefit from a good character? _____

_____

_____

7. Do you know how much you are worth? Explain. _____

_____

_____

8. Do your parents know how you act in school? Explain. _____

_____

_____

_____

9. What have you learned from this chapter? _____

_____

_____

DEFINITIONS

Norms: _____

Moral: _____

Standard: _____

Impact: _____

Abstinence: _____

WRITE A SENTENCE USING EACH WORD

Mentally _____

Cursing _____

Attributed _____

Value _____

Concepts _____

WRITE A PARAGRAPH USING THESE WORDS

Strategies—Responsibility—Upright—Productive—Idols

_____

_____

_____

_____

_____

_____

NORMS/VALUES

```
E  U  Q  L  N  H  C  C  Y  G  I  Y  L  S  E
V  P  Q  T  A  D  Y  L  U  M  C  S  A  M  S
I  R  P  D  V  R  L  H  P  R  L  B  Z  R  S
T  I  N  A  I  A  O  A  E  O  S  K  C  O  E
C  G  A  V  T  J  C  M  D  T  V  I  F  N  N
U  H  H  N  F  T  Y  I  I  J  X  L  N  F  T
D  T  E  Z  W  C  R  N  E  U  L  A  V  G  I
O  M  T  V  X  O  E  I  Y  A  J  I  J  U  A
R  E  S  P  O  N  S  I  B  I  L  I  T  Y  L
P  B  L  B  C  E  R  U  N  U  G  T  U  V  S
I  O  N  E  P  P  I  R  W  X  T  I  F  C  X
S  T  A  N  D  A  R  D  K  Z  C  E  I  E  R
B  O  H  A  B  O  V  I  P  S  E  B  D  O  M
X  W  K  T  G  S  I  R  M  L  G  V  P  L  J
S  E  I  G  E  T  A  R  T  S  N  P  M  N  J
```

ABSTINENCE	ATTRIBUTED	CURSING
ESSENTIALS	IDOLS	IMPACT
MENTALLY	MORAL	NORMS
PRODUCTIVE	RESPONSIBILITY	STANDARD
STRATEGIES	UPRIGHT	VALUE

REFLECT ON THIS CHAPTER

(Write your thoughts below)

_____

_____

_____

_____

_____

_____

_____

_____

_____

_____

_____

_____

_____

_____

_____

_____

_____

_____

_____

_____

_____

_____

_____

_____

FAILURE

n. the act of failing, or not succeeding. the act of losing strength
or weakening; the act of not doing.

Most of our teens have failed in one or more areas in their lives, during their adolescent years. They have allowed their failures to become roadblocks to where they want to be in life. Whether in their relationships, education, and friendships, or even with their families, they have experienced many setbacks. These •setbacks create sadness, physically and emotionally. Most of all, I believe these failures create •resentment towards anyone who acknowledges their shortcomings in a negative way.

In my experiences, failure causes pain from within. Many times you would notice a child laughing and carrying on but deep down inside they are carrying a load of pain from the areas in their lives where they have failed. They are really looking for some direction when it comes to how to handle their failures. Unfortunately, when they try to express themselves in those areas, they are pushed away by their teachers, parents, and friends.

(SHARING) "I am going through family problems and that's interfering with my school work. I go around covering up my feelings by smiling and trying to look good. And in reality I'm going through phases. I don't know what to do anymore. I'm struggling with a lot of problems. Everyone looks at my appearance and think I'm cute. I'm hurting inside."

—12th grade student

Reflection *(in your own words)*

_____

_____

_____

_____

_____

_____

I had a young lady who came to me after she got pregnant. She was •miserable. She did not know what to do, who to talk to, or where to go. She was not afraid of being pregnant but rather afraid of her parents' reaction to the situation. She felt like she let her parents down and failed them •tremendously. Her parents preached to her all the time about not getting pregnant, but never explained or educated her about the subject. Eventually, she mustered enough strength and courage to speak to her parents about the pregnancy. She was slapped, cursed at, and thrown out of the house because of her failures. She ended up moving in with her boyfriend's parents.

Most of the time, teens understand exactly what they have done wrong. From getting pregnant to getting a girl pregnant, failing a class, being suspended, or choosing the wrong friends, they don't need someone else •condemning them for their failures. Teens need to be loved and cared for in their failures as well as in their successes. As adults, sometimes we act like we never failed when we were teenagers. I'm not in any way applauding their failures, but understand their wrongdoings and finding helpful ways to curtail these kinds of behaviors so they don't continue. If we condemn their failures and look down on them as if they have just committed the biggest crime in the world, they will not be able to deal with their problems and the guilt at the same time. They are not •mature enough to understand failure or setback, they give up on life and that's the last thing we want our teens to do. We don't want our kids to get •discouraged because we as parents/teachers, have given up.

(SHARING) "What I am dealing with right now is my mom; she gives me a hard time. Every time we see each other, we always end up fighting because of what happened in the past. When I was in the fifth grade, I lost my virginity. I always used to skip school. There was a time that all they did was hit me instead of talking to me; I'm referring to my mom and dad. And the funny part was that I always kept on skipping. Now my dad is in jail. I don't get along with my step-dad sometimes, I just feel lonely. It's probably because I don't spend time with the people I love. I work, I have a boyfriend and it seems that he's the only one who really loves me. He's always there for me; we have been together for a year and five months. He's the only one I go to when I have a problem, because if I talk to my mom I know that she's not going to do anything for me. All she's going to do is yell at me or probably slap me!"

—11th grade student

Reflection *(in your own words)*

_____

_____

_____

_____

_____

_____

Failure is part of life; it's going to happen. What we do after we fail will •determine how long we stay in our failures. It will determine whether or not we continue to fail in that area or allow that failure to become a learning tool to better ourselves.

Most teens just need some kind of encouragement to continue their journey in life, but most of the time after they have failed in their •endeavors, we as adults or society label them by their failures. They are teenagers; they are going to fail in some regard or another. We must be there for them.

I had a tenth grader in my class during my second year of teaching at the high school level. He was a troubled child; single family home. Every month, he was suspended for fighting, cursing, or just being plain rude. Many teachers gave up on him, for good reasons I may say. I wanted to give up on him also because every time he got in trouble, I would be the one he ran too. It was taking a heavy burden on me. After a while I was beginning to assume that he didn't care or just wanted to give up because everyone else gave up on him.

I decided to do something about it. I contacted his mother one day trying to figure out why her son was behaving this way. The mother was very pleased that I called and explained to me that her son is a good boy ("yeah right," I said in my mind) and he just needed a male figure to keep him •accountable for his actions. She went on to explain how his father left him at a young age and that really discouraged him. **Fathers, where are you?** Your children need you so that they can effectively transition from adolescent to adulthood. Make yourself available to them. I believe you will see a great change in their behavior, grades, and choices.

I decided to take it upon myself to help him even though the school board was already aware of his behavior and they were in the process of •expelling him. The next day, I asked him to come to my classroom; I wanted to know what he wanted to do in life and how he planned to get there. After listening to him for about five minutes, I knew in my heart that he needed encouragement and acceptance. In order for him to achieve his goals, (and he had many) he was going to need a support group in school and at home to keep him focused. However, it was a big chance to take. It was a chance I was willing to take because of the conversation we had in the classroom. **Are you willing to encourage someone else into his or her destiny?**

I started asking all his teachers about him and what we can do to help him succeed. Of course, not all of his teachers were •enthusiastic about helping because of his track record. I decided to monitor his grades weekly and spoke to him daily about his choices. I believe after a while, he figured out someone cared for him even when he didn't care for himself. Once a child realizes that you care, he or she will put their guard down and follow instructions.

After a while, I noticed a change in him. He felt loved and encouraged even though he didn't have it all together. When he would misbehave, he would be the first to tell on himself. He would run to my classroom explaining to me how the Science or Social Studies teacher kicked him out of class. I was not easy on him. Some days I didn't allow him to enter my classroom if he got kicked out of another. I had to keep him accountable for his actions.

That year, he passed and moved on to the eleventh grade and had to make up some of the classes in the summer. I am proud to say he graduated from high school and set his eyes on college. He and I still communicate from time to time; he always sends a text asking me how I am doing. He found a friend, a brother, someone who believed in him even when others didn't. We can change our children's lives only if we believe in them even when they fail.

In my research, many teens have lost their self-esteem due to their failures. They assume life is over, or there is no way out of their situations, so they give up, and separate themselves from others (•isolation). At the end, they become •suicidal, defensive, angry, and confused. Some teens even go as far as cutting themselves with sharp objects to take away the pain, the pain of failing. None of these actions take the pain away; dealing with our failures is the only medication for advancement.

Young people, be encouraged. Don't stop living. Don't stop trying. Remember, your failures and your past experiences are not who you are. There's so much inside of you, so much •potential, so much life.

FAILURE—DISCUSSION

1. In what area(s) in your life have you *failed*? _____

_____

_____

2. Do you still think about your failures? Explain. _____

_____

_____

3. Do you allow your failures to stop you from moving forward in life? Explain. _____

_____

_____

4. List some steps you can take to overcome your failures.

    1. _____

    2. _____

    3. _____

    4 _____

5. What have you learned from your failures? _____

_____

_____

6. What have you learned from this chapter? _____

_____

_____

_____

_____

_____

_____

_____

DEFINITIONS

Setback: _____

Resentment: _____

Miserable: _____

Tremendously: _____

Condemning: _____

WRITE A SENTENCE USING EACH WORD

Mature _____

Discourage _____

Endeavors _____

Determined _____

Accountable _____

WRITE A PARAGRAPH USING THESE WORDS

Expel—Enthusiastic—Isolation—Potential—Accomplish

_____

_____

_____

_____

_____

_____

_____

_____

FAILURE

H	S	I	L	P	M	O	C	C	A	T	W	R	A	D
J	E	Y	I	K	K	R	T	E	A	T	V	C	V	E
E	M	G	N	S	M	C	N	U	N	D	C	A	R	N
R	N	K	A	U	O	D	A	E	T	O	U	T	P	I
U	M	T	O	R	E	L	M	B	U	N	L	R	O	M
T	V	T	H	A	U	T	A	N	T	L	U	E	T	R
A	I	I	V	U	N	O	T	T	E	E	Y	M	E	E
M	D	O	T	E	S	A	C	P	I	V	S	E	N	T
M	R	W	S	X	B	I	X	S	N	O	D	N	T	E
S	X	E	D	L	F	E	A	D	I	W	N	D	I	D
N	R	M	E	I	O	S	F	S	Q	D	Q	O	A	Z
E	L	B	A	R	E	S	I	M	T	I	S	U	L	H
P	Y	Y	R	I	K	S	A	J	A	I	T	S	N	J
S	V	B	T	B	V	J	G	N	U	N	C	L	V	A
C	O	N	D	E	M	N	I	N	G	P	K	Y	T	T

ACCOMPLISH ACCOUNTABLE CONDEMNING

DETERMINED DISCOURAGE ENDEAVORS

ENTHUSIASTIC EXPEL ISOLATION

MATURE MISERABLE POTENTIAL

RESENTMENT SETBACK TREMENDOUSLY

REFLECT ON THIS CHAPTER

(Write your thoughts below)

_____

_____

_____

_____

_____

_____

_____

_____

_____

_____

_____

_____

_____

_____

_____

_____

_____

_____

_____

_____

_____

_____

_____

_____

_____

SELF-ESTEEM

n. belief in oneself; self-respect; too much pride in oneself.

Many of our teens today have low self-esteem due to what they have encountered so far. Low self-esteem is like a drug; it will paralyze you to the point where life just happens instead of you making life happen. When low self-esteem sets in, a lot of thoughts enter into the minds of teens. They become stressed, which in the long run causes depression, suicide, loneliness, and broken heartedness. In the end, running away from home seems to be the only way out.

Low self-esteem will take away your belief. It will make you feel like you cannot achieve anything. It will make you feel •worthless and •unwanted.

(SHARING) "As youth, we go through problems at home as far as rape; people in their family that they're close to start •molesting them. They go through abuse. Their parents beat them severely or their parents make them go days without eating. Youth also go through drama in and out of school. People start rumors about them and they start having low self-esteem."

10th grade student

Reflection *(in your own words)*

_____

_____

_____

_____

_____

_____

_____

_____

I have had students in my class who will come to school and do absolutely nothing. They will not laugh or even speak. They are in school just because their parents force them to be there. If they had a choice, they would either be at home or hanging out with another low self-esteem student. What is causing our teens to have such low self-esteem? Is it hard for them to handle what they're going through? This generation is searching for love and comfort. Many of them have had bad relationships and experiences that left them broken, •violated, and vulnerable. They are ashamed of these experiences and question why these things have happened to them.

I remember one incident in my life when I was a teenager that caused me to have low self-esteem and become •depressed. When I was in the 10th grade, all I wanted to do was make the basketball team. I would do almost anything to make the team. I came to practice on time, I was the hardest worker, and the coach really liked the way I was playing. One day during training camp, coach asked us to run around the school five times and we would be timed. Whoever had the best time would rest for the next event.

I started running and everything was fine, I was making my time and really pushing to finish when I noticed a few of my teammates cutting through the school to make their times better. I don't know what came over me; I decided to cut through the school too. The group that cut through the school finished the course and I thought everything was okay. Then it all went downhill. The coach entered the back of the gym to talk to us. Before he gave us •instructions on the next task, he said that some of us were cut from the team because of what we had done. I said to myself, "Who told the coach that we cut through the school?" The coach caught a few of the seniors while they were cutting through the school; they •snitched on me and two other freshmen. That was so low, snitching on your teammate. My confidence level went front high to low. My self-esteem went from high to low. I could not believe that I messed up my chances of making the basketball team. I could not forgive myself. I walked all the way home with my head down trying to figure out how I could turn back the hands of time. I was upset at myself. All I wanted to do was get home and go to sleep hoping that it was all a dream. I woke up and still felt the same way. I stayed in my room the whole weekend. I didn't want to do anything. My parents asked me what happened, but I didn't have the courage to tell them that I cheated during practice and now I am off the team. I felt so low. How could I fix this? When the weekend was over, it was time to get back to school. I did not want to go because in my mind I had nothing to go to school for. When I arrived at school the assistant coach came to me saying practice is at 4:30 today in the gym and don't be late.

I told him that I was cut on Friday because I •cheated. He said he knows all about it and he was expecting me at practice.

I was so happy that the coaching staff gave us a second chance. From that moment on, my self-esteem went from low to high and I was the happiest guy in school.

As you can see, the experiences a teen •encounters can have a positive or negative impact on his/her life. Many times, all our teens need is another chance to try to get it right. Now I know some teens have gotten second, third, fourth, and fifth chances. As long as they know and understand they have been given a number of chances then they cannot complain.

Performance in school is another •hindrance that affects their self-esteem. When a student cannot understand or •comprehend assignments given to them, they will shut down and crawl under a rock if they can. First, they are afraid of being laughed at by their peers and secondly, they are ashamed that they cannot understand or comprehend the assignment. When I was at the high school level, there were many students during the FCAT (Florida Comprehension Assessment Test) testing who would purposely fight or cause trouble during the testing period. They knew that they did not understand what was on the test and would rather get in trouble, so they had an excuse not to take the test. Many times we assume that they are just troubled kids, but deep down inside they are hiding and dealing with something greater than a •standardized test.

Statistics show in many instances, that low self-esteem causes anger, rage and defiance. Low self-esteem will take away their beliefs, self-worth and ability to accomplish what is set out before them. Low self-esteem is very common in the lives of our teenagers. Do you have low self-esteem? If yes, listen to this: you have the •ability to get out of it. You cannot continue to think about the past or the things you want to change in your life. If you start thinking about what lies ahead, I can almost guarantee you that you will feel better about yourself and you will be able to continue moving •forward in your life. You cannot stay still and do nothing! You are better than that. In spite of what people may say, you can still accomplish your goals. Don't look at your current situations; learn from them and move on.

(SHARING) *"Some things that hold me back are people telling me I can't. That I am dumb and can't do anything; People putting me down, but mostly people telling me no."*

—10th grade student

95

Reflection *(in your own words)*

_____

_____

_____

_____

_____

_____

I had a chance to speak to a group of middle school students who were causing problems at school. I was asked to speak to them about their future, where and what they wanted to be in life. My first question was, "what do you want to be in life?" Most of them knew exactly what they wanted to be. However, one youngster assumed because of the decisions he had made in the past that his chances of achieving his goals were gone, so he decided to give up on everything else. Throughout the whole presentation, the only question he kept asking was "Is it too late for me to make things right and achieve what I want in life?" His questioning got so bad, I had to stop my presentation and focus on getting him to understand that it's not too late to achieve nor •overcome. He was so happy and •determined to do better. I asked him why was he so happy? "He said, because of my past experiences, I had stopped believing in myself and assumed that life was over for me. That's why I acted the way I did in the classrooms and that's why I didn't care for anybody. But now I believe that I can still achieve and be successful. Thank you."

That particular day, I knew there were others who needed to hear that they can still achieve their dreams in spite of what they have done in the past. They needed to be encouraged and I was committed to inspire as many teens as possible. You too can help somebody else believe in themselves once again. Are you willing to encourage somebody else? Well, the first thing you must do is •believe in yourself. No matter what happened in the past, you must believe that you can still achieve. You must encourage yourself, then you can help someone else. Go ahead, encourage yourself!

SELF-ESTEEM—DISCUSSION

1. Have you ever had to deal with *self-esteem*? Explain. _____
_____
_____

2. How do you deal with self-esteem? _____
_____
_____

3. Do you know anyone with low self-esteem? Explain. _____
_____
_____

4. Do you allow how you feel to determine how you act? Explain. _____
_____
_____

5. Does low self-esteem cause you to be angry? Explain. _____
_____
_____

6. Have you ever been depressed? If yes, explain. _____
_____
_____

7. What causes you to have low self-esteem? _____
_____
_____

8. List some steps you can take to overcome low self-esteem?

   1. _____
   2. _____
   3. _____
   4 _____

9. What have you learned from this chapter? _____

_____

_____

DEFINITIONS

Worthless: _____

Unwanted: _____

Molesting: _____

Depress: _____

Violate: _____

WRITE A SENTENCE USING EACH WORD

Instruction _____

Cheat _____

Encounter_____

Hindrance_____

Comprehend _____

WRITE A PARAGRAPH USING THESE WORDS

Standardized—Ability—Forward—Believe—Overcome—Determine

_____

_____

_____

_____

_____

SELF-ESTEEM

ACROSS
1. To make someone feel very sad or hopeless
3. To assist the progress of something
5. Incompetent, or totally lacking good, attractive or admirable qualities
6. Unwelcome
8. To treat something sacred with lack of respect
9. Someone or something that prevents or makes it difficult to do something
10. To accept that something is true or real

DOWN
2. A meeting with someone or something, usually unexpected
4. To influence or give form to something
7. To force unwanted sexual attention on someone

REFLECT ON THIS CHAPTER

(Write your thoughts below)

_____

_____

_____

_____

BULLYING

n. a person who likes to hurt or frighten those who are smaller or weaker

There are many types of bullying. Bullying can be verbal, or physical. Why do kids bully? Is it a lack of self-esteem? Do they want to be accepted? Are they experiencing some kind of bullying at home? Maybe they would rather bully than be bullied. According to Frank Peretti, a New York Times best-selling author of Christian fiction, there are two basic reasons why kids bully. One reason a child bullies is because he (or she) "has a deep troubling need of his own" and is picked on or feels that he does not have a very successful life. Bullies may be experiencing trouble at home, be •underachievers in school, and for whatever reason they feel they have to make themselves better by picking on someone else. On the outside bullies may look fine, but they may be very lonely or may •deliberately try to hurt themselves or have trouble eating or sleeping. Whatever the reason may be, kids are being bullied every day. Have you ever been bullied by another? How does it feel?

I have had a few occasions where I was the victim of bullying. I could not understand why someone wanted to hurt me. I really did not know anybody; coming from another country did not help. When I first arrived in this country, I found myself at war with others because of where I came from. People wanted to fight me just because I was from Haiti. It was a hard time for my Haitian friends and me. There were days where we had to run for our lives because someone wanted to jump us or fight us just because of where we came from. I came to find out that some of the same kids that wanted to fight us were undercover Haitians. They figured if they would fight with the other groups, they would be free from harm. They would rather bully than be bullied.

Many of our teens today are being bullied because they are from another county. Many days I was afraid to attend school because of what was going on in school. I left my country because I wanted to go to school but couldn't because there were no schools. Now I am in a country where there is school but I was afraid to attend because of what may happen to me. Throughout the day, you would hear about kids getting jumped in the bathrooms. There was a fight every day. Every day, someone was bullied for who they are or where they came from. I guess nothing has changed because after twenty plus years, kids are still being bullied.

(SHARING) "The girls in school don't like me. When they see me, they either turn their faces and talk about me or just plan rude. They call me names because I don't look like them or talk like them." —8th grade student

Reflection *(in your own words)*

_____

_____

_____

_____

_____

_____

_____

_____

I attended a middle school in the inner city area of Miami Florida. There was a bridge that connected the housing projects to the school. This bridge allows students from the housing projects to cross over to the school in a shorter period of time. The bridge had a river underneath with alligators going back and forth. The kids who lived in the projects would control who crossed the bridge. If they had issues with you and you tried to cross the bridge, they would fight you, take your shoes and throw you over the bridge. If you wanted to get to the other side and didn't want to cross the bridge, you would have to go all the way around the block just to get to the other side. It was a scary time. Being bullied is not fun. It causes pain and •depression from within.

One day, I had to cross over to attend after school tutoring. I didn't want to walk around the street just to get to the other side. I decided to cross the bridge. I was so afraid! I started walking towards the bridge and noticed no one was there. I was relieved and happy. Unfortunately, that peace of mind only lasted a little while. As I stepped on the bridge, a few of the boys who lived there were walking towards the bridge. I was so confused! I didn't want to run because that might give them a reason to chase me and throw me over. I kept on walking, and when I got real close to them, one of them said that I had nice shoes. I said thank you and kept walking. The thought of me being tossed into the river became more and more real. When I arrived at the center for tutoring, my older brother was surprised that I was there so quick. He asked me which way I took to get there, I said the bridge. He was •stunned that I took that route and nothing happened to me. He made sure that day that I understood the danger of crossing that bridge. When teens are being bullied, they develop a mindset to survive, not to learn. Their focus is on how to stay alive, how to stay away from certain people, and how to make it to the next day.

(SHARING) "Sometimes I don't want to come to school because I am afraid of bullies. They are everywhere." —10th grade student

Reflection *(in your own words)*

_____

_____

_____

_____

_____

_____

_____

After arriving at the center for tutoring, I felt safe. My brother was there and I knew he would protect me. One of the boys from the bridge followed me because he noticed I had a watch that he wanted. He came up behind me •demanding my watch. I told him that he could not have it. He was very upset. He tried to get close to me but I kicked him in the face. He left and ran towards the housing projects. We knew exactly what he went to do. Everybody was saying to us that we should leave immediately before he comes back with ten others. My brother and I ran from the center into the street towards our house. We were about 30 to 40 minutes away from home. We decided to hide in the back of a local supermarket. We were so afraid. We did not want to get jumped by him and his friends. So we waited until nighttime and decided to make the journey home. It was a long journey. It felt like we were being followed but we finally made it home safely.

We did not attend school for about three days because we wanted to let things die down before we went back. Because of bullying, we had to miss three days of our education. It is sad, but teens are staying home just to stay away from being bullied. Being bullied is embarrassing. It makes you feel •powerless. I never understood why others stood there and did nothing.

(SHARING) "I would rather bully than being bullied. It's embarrassing!"

—12th grade student

Reflection *(in your own words)*

_____

_____

_____

_____

_____

_____

_____

_____

Bullying must stop! Nothing about bullying is cool. It only seems ok when you are the one doing the bullying. Throughout my experiences in the schools, I had a chance to speak to teens that had experienced bullying in one form or another. One thing they always said was that they would never forget it. It is •shameful and they wished it never happened. I've been bullied a few times during my adolescent years and I still remember the faces of those teenagers. I don't have any •resentment towards them, however, I still remember their faces.

Most of the time, teens want to report bullying, however, they are afraid of being called a snitch. So they continue to live with the embarrassment of being bullied and laughed at. This must stop!

BULLYING—DISCUSSION

1. Have you ever been bullied? If yes, explain. _____

_____

_____

2. Have you ever bullied anyone? If yes, why?_____

_____

_____

3. How did it feel to bully someone or be bullied? _____

_____

_____

4. Do you know the effects of a person that's being bullied? Explain _____

_____

_____

5. Can you relate to the stories from this chapter? _____

If yes, explain. _____

_____

_____

_____

6. What have you learned from this chapter? _____

_____

_____

_____

DEFINITIONS

Underachiever: _____

Deliberately: _____

Furtive: _____

Depression: _____

Stunned: _____

WRITE A SENTENCE USING EACH WORD

Demanding _____

Powerless _____

Shame _____

Resentment _____

Bully _____

WRITE A PARAGRAPH USING THESE WORDS

Dishonor—Embarrassment—Unworthiness—Insult—Attention

_____

_____

_____

_____

_____

_____

_____

_____

_____

_____

BULLYING

```
T  R  G  Z  E  G  L  X  D  N  G  Y  T  U  P
I  A  X  G  N  I  R  J  B  Y  D  N  C  W  D
I  U  N  D  E  R  A  C  H  I  E  V  E  R  D
N  R  N  Z  I  H  S  I  E  M  D  R  P  G  E
F  O  W  W  V  R  N  T  S  M  E  B  N  O  L
U  U  I  S  O  S  C  S  U  S  A  I  B  S  I
R  L  B  T  U  R  A  Q  E  N  D  H  E  S  B
T  J  C  L  N  R  T  N  H  N  N  D  S  E  E
I  C  T  Q  R  E  T  H  A  N  R  E  T  L  R
V  Z  J  A  U  M  T  M  I  V  R  A  D  R  A
E  U  B  C  E  Q  E  T  W  N  F  C  V  E  T
X  M  P  N  U  D  R  X  A  F  E  M  G  W  E
E  O  T  D  I  S  H  O  N  O  R  S  L  O  L
N  O  I  S  S  E  R  P  E  D  J  B  S  P  Y
Y  L  L  U  B  C  F  B  E  B  O  Q  R  D  U
```

ATTENTION	BULLY	DELIBERATELY
DEMANDING	DEPRESSION	DISHONOR
EMBARRASSMENT	FURTIVE	INSULT
POWERLESS	RESENTMENT	SHAME
STUNNED	UNDERACHIEVER	UNWORTHINESS

106

REFLECT ON THIS CHAPTER

(Write your thoughts below)

_____

_____

_____

_____

_____

_____

_____

_____

_____

_____

_____

_____

_____

_____

_____

_____

_____

_____

_____

_____

_____

_____

_____

_____

_____

FINANCES

*n. All the money or income that a government, company, person, etc.
has ready for use. The business of taking care of money matters.*

Many of our teens today are not thinking about the future when it comes to finances. What they are doing is •entertaining themselves with things that will only last a little while. They are spending all of their money on clothes, shoes, cell phones, accessories, hair extensions, going to the mall, eating out, and so on. The 2010 Teens and Personal Finance Survey stated that boys and girls spend their money in different ways. Girls spent 68% of their money on clothing while boys spent 38% of their money on clothing. Girl spent 45% of their money on music while boys spent 35% of their money on music. Moreover, girls spent 13% of their money on video games and boys spent 50% of their money on video games, just to name a few. At this rate, they will never be able to save any money for the future. Many of them don't even have a bank account. Teens should take their time to open a bank account to have a better understanding of their spending. Parents play a big role in their children's finances since they are the ones most of the time •providing them with the money. Parents, take your kids to the bank and open a bank account. Teach them how to manage the account which in the long run will teach how to be responsible with money.

When you walk around the hallways in the middle and high schools, what you see are expensive name brand clothes and shoes; some are worth more than $150 dollars. I know some teens that have a new pair of Jordans every week. Imagine where they would be in their finances if they saved some of that money. You also notice teens with cell phones that adults with jobs don't have. Where are they getting their money? Most of them don't work! It's more important to get the latest shoes, than to get a higher GPA. Where have we gone wrong? Teens will pressure their parents to get them the most expensive clothes or shoes to wear to school. I remember when I was starting to get •familiar with the way things were done here in this country. I no longer wanted the pro-wings (A name brand shoe from Payless) my parents would get me nor the no name brand clothes. The kids who wore the no name brands got little play from the girls and were looked at as poor and dirty. So I pressured my parents to get the nice stuff. Even though I did not get them all the time, I was able to get what I wanted some of the time.

When I was in college, I was blessed enough to get a basketball •scholarship which covered all of my expenses from tuition to food, to books, and room and board. I also qualified to receive financial aid from the government. In addition, I had a part time job working in the gym. Whenever the financial aid would arrive, I would go to the mall and buy whatever I wanted since the scholarship would cover my schooling. I mean I was living large. I had at least 20 pair of shoes with matching outfits. I was balling! When I went to the gym, I was matching from head to toe. Blue shorts, blue Jordan's, and blue top. It went like that for every color. My friends would look for me to see what I would be wearing the next day. After a while, I felt like I had to keep up this look because that's what I was known for and I liked the •attention I was getting.

Today I regret every moment of it because I have nothing to show for it. All the shoes are worn out; all the clothes are outdated, and all the monies are gone. I calculated from the time I started college to the time I graduated. I spent around $25,000 on clothes, shoes and other material things. If I only knew, I would have saved up my money, put it in the bank or the stock market, which in ten years would have grown with interest. Today I would have so much money that I would be able to have anything I wanted. I would have enough money to start my own business.

No one told me about saving, the stock market, or a savings account. Or maybe I was not listening. Well, I am now telling you! Stop spending your money on things that will eventually •perish. I am not saying not to look good or be cool. All I am saying is saving your money is a good •principle to have at a young age. For example, you can buy what you want one week and the next week you can save that money in the bank. You don't have to have a new outfit every week. Preparing for your future now is the best thing you can do to better yourself today. What would you rather do—look good now or be broke later? Or look okay now and be rich later? Well, whichever way you decide to have it begins today! Pay close attention to how you understand money and how you spend money.

FINANCES—DISCUSSION

1. How much money do you spend a week? _____

2. Do you have an allowance? _____ If yes, how much?_____

3. List some of the things you spend your money on:

   1. _____

   2. _____

   3. _____

   4 _____

   5. _____

4. Do you have a bank account? _____

5. How much money you think you can save in a month? Explain _____

   _____

   _____

6. List some things you've got to have. _____

   _____

   _____

   _____

7. Do you feel you have to buy the name brand clothes/shoes? Why?_____

   _____

   _____

8. After reading this chapter, what have you learned? _____

   _____

   _____

   _____

   _____

DEFINITIONS

Entertainment: _____

Provision: _____

Familiar: _____

Attention: _____

Perish: _____

WRITE A SENTENCE USING EACH WORD

Scholarship _____

Principle _____

Finance _____

Responsibility _____

Expensive _____

WRITE A PARAGRAPH USING THESE WORDS

Tuition—Financial—Quality—Saving—Preparation

_____

_____

_____

_____

_____

_____

_____

_____

_____

FINANCES

```
E  L  Y  Y  O  K  G  S  F  E  P  E  A  I  E
C  K  A  C  D  N  Y  A  V  R  Z  L  T  H  N
N  G  U  I  I  F  M  I  E  P  O  P  T  K  T
A  F  H  V  C  I  S  P  P  C  Z  I  E  Y  E
N  A  A  C  L  N  A  L  K  N  J  C  N  Q  R
I  S  A  I  E  R  A  H  G  I  C  N  T  V  T
F  Q  A  P  A  S  P  N  M  F  L  I  I  D  A
Y  R  X  T  D  P  E  R  I  S  H  R  O  Z  I
Z  E  I  L  U  X  U  Y  K  F  W  P  N  X  N
N  O  I  T  I  U  T  E  T  K  U  R  P  G  M
N  D  E  P  R  O  V  I  S  I  O  N  R  K  E
R  E  S  P  O  N  S  I  B  I  L  I  T  Y  N
P  F  P  Q  Z  D  W  W  O  Y  D  A  I  R  T
P  I  H  S  R  A  L  O  H  C  S  K  U  N  Z
N  T  B  C  H  G  I  G  K  L  K  I  F  Q  E
```

ATTENTION	ENTERTAINMENT	EXPENSIVE
FAMILIAR	FINANCE	FINANCIAL
PERISH	PREPARATION	PRINCIPLE
PROVISION	QUALITY	RESPONSIBILITY
SAVING	SCHOLARSHIP	TUITION

REFLECT ON THIS CHAPTER

(Write your thoughts below)

_____

_____

_____

_____

_____

_____

_____

_____

_____

_____

_____

_____

_____

_____

_____

_____

_____

_____

_____

_____

_____

_____

_____

_____

_____

_____

ACCOUNTABILITY

Adj. expected to account for what one does; responsible for one action.

You are where you are today because of the decisions you've made in the past. Whether good or bad, your decisions and experiences have •contributed to where you are now. Too many times, our teens have used what happened to them in the past as an •excuse to where they are now. Some of them have a solid case. However, they have to take some responsibility for their future. Today's teens blame everybody else but themselves.

I had a student in my class who came to school late every day, sat in the back, and never turned in his work. He was very funny and everybody loved him. I had a pretty good relationship with him. I like to laugh; he liked to make people laugh. One day, while preparing for a class test, I asked him if he was ready for the test and he said yes. I asked him how, since he doesn't turn in any assignments. He nodded his head and said "I got this!" The test was scheduled for Friday, therefore he had all week to study and be ready for it. Friday came and he sat down and took the test. In my class, we graded tests immediately. He had the worst score in the class—a 47% on the test, •equivalent to an "F". He was very upset because he got a low grade. How could he be upset? He did nothing to prepare himself to pass that test. He was so upset with me because in his head, I gave him the "F". He was so upset that he was •threatening me. I truly didn't understand his mindset. What was he expecting? He sat there for the whole week and did not study knowing he had a test on Friday. Throughout his life, he never took the responsibility or the accountability for where he was in life. He always blamed others for his actions. He did not understand that he's the one who controls his successes and failures. I always tell my students that if a teacher dislikes you for any reason, but you always turn in your assignments, like you or not, he or she has to give you what you earn.

Too many times students allow others to dictate their •achievements. YOUR achievement is in YOUR hands. No one can take away what you have earned. So if you do nothing, expect nothing. On the other hand, if you do a lot then you should expect a lot. I never understood why students get upset during report card season. Whatever grades that are on that report card are based on what they have done during the semester. As teachers, we cannot give a student an "F" just because we don't like the kid. For the most part, the grades on the report cards usually reflect test scores, homework, class assignments, and student's behavior throughout the semester. If you got an "F", it's because you did nothing during that particular semester. You can only blame yourself! I know there are a few •exceptions; nevertheless, it is the student's responsibility to make up any missing assignments.

Being responsible and accountable for your actions is vital to your growth as a teen. These •attributes will keep you on the path to success. If you want to succeed in life, you have to take into account the things you have done wrong and be mature enough to change them and not allow them to stop you from achieving.

I have heard all the excuses in the world and some teens would say things like, "The reason why I don't care about anybody is because my dad left my mom when I was five years old and she had to raise me on her own." I always tell my students that there are teens in Africa who have it worse than they do and they still go to school because they know this is the only way out. I never allowed any of my students to use that excuse. I know what happened in the past may have contributed to where you are now but how long are you going to use that excuse? It's like a woman who gains a little weight during her pregnancy still using the excuse, "it's baby fat," when their child is six years old. It's time for you to use your hurts, pain, and struggles to •motivate yourself to achieve your goals. If you do, you will overcome your fears; what was meant to keep you down, will propel you to succeed.

ACCOUNTABILITY—DISCUSSION

1. Do you think about the consequences of your actions? Explain. _____

_____

_____

2. Do you take responsibility for your actions? Explain. _____

_____

_____

3. If you failed a class or made a bad choice, whose to blame? Explain. _____

_____

_____

4. Do you blame your past experiences for your lack of production? Explain. _____

_____

_____

5. Do you blame your teachers for your low grades? Explain. _____

_____

_____

6. What have you learned from this chapter? _____

_____

_____

7. In your own words define accountability? _____

_____

_____

_____

_____

_____

DEFINITIONS

Contribute: _____

Excuses: _____

Equivalent: _____

Achievement: _____

WRITE A SENTENCE USING EACH WORD

Exception _____

Attribute_____

Responsibility _____

Motivate _____

Consequence _____

WRITE A PARAGRAPH USING THESE WORDS

Decision—Behavior—Education—Relationship—Accountable

_____

_____

_____

_____

_____

_____

_____

_____

_____

_____

_____

ACCOUNTABILITY

```
T  B  A  M  V  K  I  R  L  V  Y  M  F  C  C
O  N  I  C  E  X  C  E  P  T  I  O  N  O  T
M  E  E  B  C  Z  L  S  H  I  C  U  R  N  N
E  D  A  M  T  O  N  P  W  U  C  E  X  T  E
C  U  R  T  E  H  U  O  Z  E  L  V  M  R  L
N  C  O  Y  T  V  W  N  I  A  E  J  T  I  A
E  A  I  P  Z  R  E  S  T  S  Z  X  D  B  V
U  T  V  L  X  T  I  I  J  A  I  A  R  U  I
Q  I  A  G  R  X  O  B  H  T  B  C  W  T  U
E  O  H  H  R  N  P  I  U  C  E  L  E  E  Q
S  N  E  D  S  C  W  L  Y  T  A  V  E  D  E
N  J  B  H  C  G  O  I  K  P  E  F  Q  P  I
O  P  I  X  N  K  E  T  A  V  I  T  O  M  Y
C  P  M  I  P  R  M  Y  E  X  C  U  S  E  S
G  N  I  N  E  T  A  E  R  H  T  Y  F  U  N
```

ACCOUNTABLE	ACHIEVEMENT	ATTRIBUTE
BEHAVIOR	CONSEQUENCE	CONTRIBUTE
DECISION	EDUCATION	EQUIVALENT
EXCEPTION	EXCUSES	MOTIVATE
RELATIONSHIP	RESPONSIBILITY	THREATENING

REFLECT ON THIS CHAPTER

(Write your thoughts below)

FOCUS

n. to fix or settle on some one thing; to center or concentrate

What are you thinking about? What are you focusing on these days? Is it sex? Is it your failures? Do you want to be loved? Maybe you're thinking about your troubles at home! Or maybe you are thinking about your father who you have not seen for the last 3 years because he is locked up in jail. Maybe you don't have these issues to think about. All I know is many of you are not thinking about your education, are you? You are not thinking about your grades and how they will affect you in the future. You are not thinking about how you can get pregnant or catch a sexually •transmitted disease when you're sleeping with that young man or young woman. Maybe you are thinking about giving up on life or dropping out of school because you cannot handle the pressures at home and school. What are you thinking about? Whatever you're thinking about, you will have to refocus your thoughts and energy on what's important. You cannot focus on your past relationships, failures, hurts, and experiences, for they are in the past. If you continue to focus on them, they will become a barrier to your future.

(SHARING) "I am not focusing on the right things these days. I have so much going on in my life. My education is the last thing on my mind."   —12th grade student

Reflection *(in your own words)*

_____

_____

_____

_____

_____

_____

When I look around the schools, teenagers have a hard time staying focused. Their minds run •rampant on everything that's going on around them. Redirecting their focus will take some time, however, it can be done.

Teenagers need to speak out their problems so these issues can be resolved and allow them to move on. However, finding someone to express these feelings and experiences without judging them is challenging. They will carry their thoughts in their minds for as long as it takes until they find a place or a person who can relate to them and not be judgmental.

After reading the chapters in this book, can you see what teenagers are focusing on? What is the cause behind their thoughts? One thing I have learned is that if I focus on one thing for a long time, that particular thing becomes part of me. For example, if you think about stealing all the time, the next chance you get to steal, you will do it. If you think about having sex all day long (which most of you do), when the next chance presents itself, you will have a hard time saying no. So as you can see, the things you focus on will eventually become your reality. It's time to change your focus; it's time to redirect your focus on positive things that will benefit you in the future not for a moment!

(SHARING) *"Sometimes I need to be reminded by my parents about the things I should be doing and where I want to be five years from now. As teenagers, so much goes in and out of our minds daily. It's hard to stay focused."* —12th grade student

Reflection *(in your own words)*

_____

_____

_____

_____

_____

_____

_____

_____

When I was in high school, I was kicked off the basketball team three times. Once, because I cheated while we were training and the other two times because I was •ineligible to play. All I did day and night was focus on basketball. Basketball was always on my mind. Even when I was in class, my focus was on basketball. I ended up failing three of my classes and was kicked off the team. Only then, did I start thinking about my education. Many times we want something so bad that we allow that particular thing to •distract us from achieving. I eventually got back on the team, but unfortunately it cost me a lot of pain.

It is very important that we focus on the right things. Our dreams and goals should always be in our thoughts. However, we have to focus on how we can achieve these dreams and goals. Don't just be a dreamer; be a doer. Many times we say what we want to do or be in life, but get •sidetracked with life itself. When I want to stay focused on a task or goal, I write it down and print it in large print. I tape it to my door or office, this way I will never forget it. Are you willing to redirect your focus? You need to! The time to be what you want to be starts TODAY, not tomorrow. Get focused on your goals and be determined to achieve them. No matter what happens, STAY FOCUSED.

FOCUS—DISCUSSION

1. What are you thinking about? _____

_____

_____

2. List some distractions that prevent you from staying focused.

   1. _____

   2. _____

   3. _____

   4 _____

   5. _____

3. What do you plan to do about your list of distractions? _____

_____

_____

4. What are the advantages of staying focused? _____

_____

_____

5. What are the outcomes of losing focus? _____

_____

_____

6. What have you learned from this chapter? _____

_____

_____

_____

_____

_____

_____

DEFINITIONS

Concentrate:_____

Transmit: _____

Rampant: _____

Ineligible: _____

Distract: _____

WRITE A SENTENCE USING EACH WORD

Sidetrack _____

Diversion _____

Focus _____

Education_____

Redirect _____

WRITE A PARAGRAPH USING THESE WORDS

Dreamer—Goals—Careers—Refocus—Barrier

_____

_____

_____

_____

_____

_____

_____

_____

_____

FOCUS

T	N	A	P	M	A	R	M	K	J	S	E	V	R	G
K	U	M	J	S	Y	A	C	C	B	U	D	P	E	T
X	I	Y	Y	I	U	Q	T	A	W	C	U	J	F	C
I	L	O	N	N	G	C	R	C	A	O	C	Y	O	A
M	K	I	R	F	M	R	Y	Q	E	F	A	D	C	R
E	V	D	N	I	I	O	C	Z	Z	R	T	D	U	T
C	O	N	C	E	N	T	R	A	T	E	I	D	S	S
L	S	U	R	Y	L	Q	S	I	R	V	O	D	M	I
T	L	E	X	Q	R	I	M	L	E	E	N	A	E	D
Z	Y	M	O	R	J	S	G	R	A	A	E	V	P	R
N	X	Q	F	V	N	A	S	I	K	O	U	R	U	F
T	F	L	T	A	X	I	P	Z	B	H	G	A	S	I
V	Z	S	R	I	O	S	V	Y	P	L	F	K	A	A
L	U	T	Z	N	D	D	R	E	A	M	E	R	Z	M
F	V	K	C	A	R	T	E	D	I	S	C	A	E	K

BARRIER	CAREERS	CONCENTRATE
DISTRACT	DIVERSION	DREAMER
EDUCATION	FOCUS	GOALS
INELIGIBLE	RAMPANT	REDIRECT
REFOCUS	SIDETRACK	TRANSMIT

REFLECT ON THIS CHAPTER

(Write your thoughts below)

CONCLUSION

Understanding the mindset of our teens is a big component in effectively having any success in dealing with their issues. I truly appreciate the time I spent as a substitute and as a full-time teacher. I truly have a different view of the way teenagers act and the reasons behind their actions. I have a great deal of respect for any teenager who's trying to make it in today's society. It is hard, however, I know many of them are overcoming their pains, struggles, and striving to live for the future. Writing this book was a challenge for me because I found myself reliving each scenario and conversation I experienced.

Four years ago, I took on a journey to write this book, to write about the things I saw and experienced as an employee of the Broward County School Board. Some were good and some were bad, however, I am a better person because of these experiences. I have a better view on teens as well as how to talk and relate to them from their perspective. I wish parents would take the time out of their busy schedules to come to their children's schools sometimes. Not for a parent conference, but just to see exactly what goes on in the classrooms, the hallways, and so on. This way they would truly understand the teenager they have at home is completely different from the teenager at school. To see firsthand all that teens and teachers have to handle and deal with on a day-to-day basis. I hope that parents all the over the country read this book and allow it to be a guide and resource when dealing with their teens. I hope teachers all over the country will read this book to have a better understanding of what's expected of them as teachers and how to better communicate with their students. It's going to take parents and teachers to come together to have a lasting, powerful, and positive effect on our teens.

When you look around the schools and our communities, we can see that our youth needs help. They want to be understood and accepted for who they are. As parents, teachers, and counselors, let us take time to truly understand the reasons behind their outbursts. Let us take the time to truly understand the reasons behind their anger and lack of focus. There's more to them than what they are showing. Teenagers will not share their deepest thoughts with anyone they think will not understand what they are going through, or with anyone who will talk down to them. At the end of the day, teens will talk to whomever they have a relationship with. They will express themselves to people they can trust. Can you be trusted?

Thank you for allowing me to share my stories and experiences with you. I hope after you have read this book, you will be more in tune and more open to the way you deal with this generation. I hope before you make any judgmental decisions or actions towards them, you have taken the time to hear and understand where that particular action you are confronting comes from and how to respond to it.

If you are a student between 5th and 12th grade, I hope that you are aware of your choices and understand that everything you do now will have an effect on you in one way or another.

Remember to be yourself. Think before you act. Think about the consequences of your actions. Think about the relationships you are having. Think about the people you are having these relationships with. Are they worth your time, body, and mind? Are you ready and willing to deal with the consequence of giving up your body? It's already hard enough to make it as a teen in this society; don't allow your youth to add more pain and struggle to your future.

Remember, what you do today will eventually be part of your tomorrow. What do you want your tomorrow to look like? Well, whatever it may be, it starts today. Don't wait another day to start making the right decisions. Every day you waste, you waste making the right decisions. After reading this book, if you notice you are on the wrong track, it's not too late to get on the right track. "LETS GO!"

CONCLUSION

1. After reading this book, what have you learned? _____

_____

_____

_____

2. What information caught your attention?_____

_____

_____

_____

3. What do you plan to do with this information? _____

_____

_____

4. What area in your life do you feel you need to change? Explain. _____

_____

_____

_____

5. How do you plan to change them? Explain. _____

_____

_____

_____

6. Where do you see yourself five years from today? _____

_____

_____

_____

_____

NOTES

WHAT'S ON YOUR MIND?

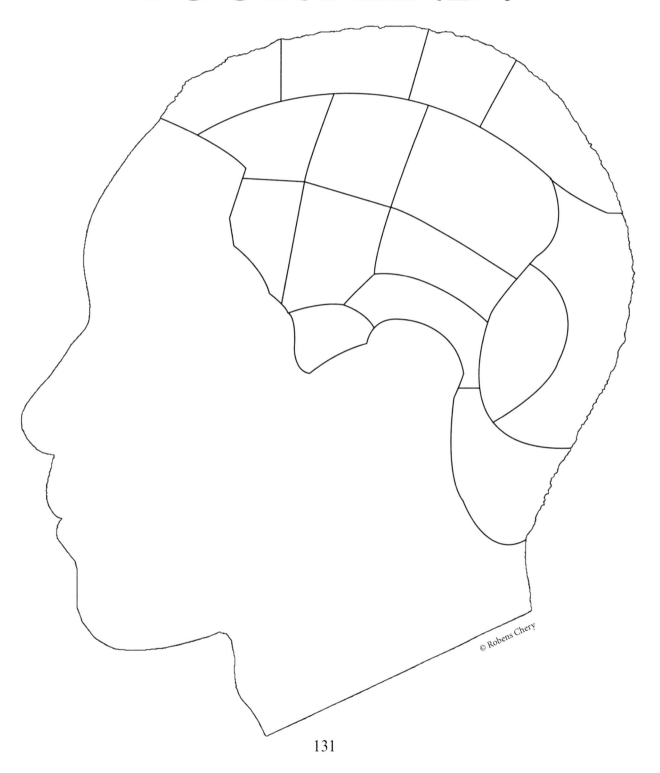

© Robens Chery

131